UNDERSTANDING
THE
GLOBAL WARMING HOAX

EXPANDED AND UPDATED

Also by Leo Johnson

The Layman's Guide to Understanding the Global Warming Hoax

UNDERSTANDING
THE
GLOBAL WARMING HOAX

EXPANDED AND UPDATED

LEO JOHNSON

RED ANVIL PRESS
OAKLAND

RED ANVIL PRESS
Red Anvil books are available from your favorite bookstore, amazon.com, or
from our 24 hour order line: 1.800.431.1579

Library of Congress Control Number: 9781934956137
Publisher's Catalog-in-Publication Data
Understanding The Global Warming Hoax/
Leo Johnson
ISBN-13: 978-1-934956-13-7
ISBN-10: 1-934956-13-9

1. Global Warming.
2. Climate Change.
3. Junk Science.
4. Hoax.
5. Politics.
I. Title

This book was written, printed and bound in the United States of America.

To the thousands of global warming skeptics
who refused to be silenced
and
my best critic, Barbara

CONTENTS

PREFACE

This is a story about global warming—both myth and reality. Reality is based solely on scientific evidence; myth is based on junk science, apocalyptic speculation, and fear.

It is also a modern-day version of the story of Galileo, who was accused of heresy for suggesting that the Earth was not the center of the universe. The heretic of today is called a "climate change denier," one who does not accept that man is the cause of global warming and accused of crimes against the environment. Unlike Galileo who was imprisoned, today's heretics are subject to intimidation, personal attacks, slander, censorship, loss of government funding, elimination of their positions as climatologists, even death threats. Nuremberg-type trials have been suggested.

For providing the stimulus to assemble this guide, I want to thank all those who have created, promoted, or contributed to the hoax of man-made global warming:

1. The United Nations Intergovernmental Panel on Climate Change (IPCC) for using fraudulent and erroneous data and misrepresentation in their reports;

2. The UN's Yvo de Boer for criminalizing dissent on global warming;

3. The IPCC's Rajendra Pachauri for comparing skeptics to Hitler;

4. Senator John McCain for pushing his Kyoto-like mandates and his denigrating comments against dissenting scientists;

5. Senators Olympia Snowe and John D. Rockefeller IV for intimidating Exxon Mobil for funding "climate change denier" groups;

6. The scientists who tarnished the credibility of science by promoting the global warming scam;

7. Alarmist climate modeler James Hansen for his numerous false predictions and doctoring NASA's global temperature data;

8. Network and cable television for their constant one-sided drumbeats of misinformation, propaganda and fearmongering on global warming;

9. Al Gore for his book of fiction on global warming;

10. The newspaper editors who reject most if not all letters of dissent on global warming (the New York Times, Wall Street Journal, Star-Ledger, Bernardsville News, and many others).

Those who complete reading this layman's guide will know and understand the evidence that scientists have gathered about all of the factors that govern Earth's climate. Carbon dioxide in the atmosphere is not one of them. With the knowledge acquired, you will win any debate on the subject of global warming whether it is with family members, friends, teachers in the classroom, professors in academia, environmental extremists, politicians, members of the United Nations panel on climate change, or Al Gore.

ONE

Creating a Global Warming Myth

How have the myths of global warming been created? An illustration of how one of the global warming myths might have been created is as follows:

There is a report of a thinning of the ice along the southern shoreline of Greenland. A computer programmer is asked: "What if the entire ice cap over Greenland melts?" A supercomputer spits out the result that sea level will rise 20 feet and New York City will be under water. The melting of Greenland ice is adopted by alarmists as a consequence of man-made global warming.

The media join the deception by providing visual images in support of the illusion. Special effects create scenes of tidal waves crashing down the streets of Manhattan for movies and television "documentaries," and Al Gore incorporates a claim of a 20-foot rise in sea level into his movie An Inconvenient Truth.

TWO

Fear and Hysteria

Consider the climate alarms that have been sounded since the 1970s. The next ice age is coming! The Earth has a fever! Which is it? After a thirty-year cooling period from 1940 to the 1970s, the public was warned of the coming of the next ice age. A decade later, when an increase in atmospheric carbon dioxide was detected, the century-old theory of Arrhenius was resurrected to claim global warming due to greenhouse gases would increase Earth's temperature by as much as 5°C (9°F). Many of the global warming alarmists of today were advocates of the ice age prediction. The failure to provide proof in support of these predictions, both then and now, makes clear that there are charlatans in the new and growing climate change industry.

To generate fear and hysteria, the notion of global warming due to greenhouse gases has been expanded by calling it climate change, so that global warming could be blamed for a litany of natural disasters—droughts, floods, rising sea levels and flooding of coastal regions, more frequent and more intense hurricanes, Hurricane Katrina (according to Al Gore), catastrophic forest fires, mass extinction of species, even volcanic eruptions and the undersea earthquakes that produced the Indonesian tsunami of 2004.

The term climate change is also used to permit global cooling to be blamed on global warming. As the next Little Ice Age approaches, or when hell freezes over, the alarmists will claim it was caused by global warming. Carbon dioxide and the greenhouse effect is the cause of everything. Since humans produce carbon dioxide by burning fossil fuels, humans are to blame for every climatic and natural disaster.

The fantasy and deceit are magnified by television media into horror shows with computer-generated special effects portraying New York City under water and file footage video showing calving of glaciers, a lonely polar bear, raging forest fires, Hurricane Katrina, the earthquake-generated tsunami in Indonesia, and so forth.

The propaganda portion of these programs begins with the alarmists favorite word "if." When one hears or reads the word "if," one can be certain that what follows is Hollywood fantasy, not scientific fact. Global warming hysteria is based on "if."

The programs consistently conclude with predictions that natural phenomena will be made worse with global warming.

THREE

COMPUTER MODELS OF GLOBAL WARMING BY GREENHOUSE GASES

The theory of global warming due to greenhouse gases in the atmosphere that is used in computer simulations of climate is as follows: An increase in a greenhouse gas in the atmosphere (CO_2, methane, ozone, etc.) causes a slight increase in Earth's surface temperature through the greenhouse effect, in which thermal radiation from the earth's surface is absorbed by the gases in the atmosphere and reradiated back to the Earth's surface. The small increase causes increased evaporation of the dominant greenhouse gas, water vapor. To amplify the small surface temperature increase produced by carbon dioxide, the computer simulations assign a positive feedback to water vapor, so that the surface temperature is increased by about a factor of 3, producing the exaggerated predictions of future global temperature characteristic of climate models—and a runaway heating of the Earth's surface. In other words, the models assume that more evaporation of water produces more warming that triggers a thermal avalanche. The models require that the stability of Earth's climate is so precarious that a slight variation in atmospheric composition will plunge the climate into chaos. Earth's climate history demonstrates a much greater resilience to such changes.

Climate models are constructed by software engineers, not scientists. Computer programmers are not qualified in the climate science disciplines of climatology, meteorology, atmospheric physics, astrophysics, marine sciences, geology, chemistry, physics, and a host of other disciplines relevant to Earth's climate.

All of these climate simulations contain a black box of ignorance: lack of scientific data; unknowns; assumptions; lack of understanding of meteorological phenomena, the role of water vapor, the influence of solar activity and cosmic rays; and so forth. The black box guarantees that every simulation of future climate is wrong. They all fail the test of replicating the global temperature behavior of the last century.

The failure to understand the role of water vapor and clouds in regulating Earth's climate constitutes the most important fatal flaw in computer simulations of climate. For example, since a small increase in temperature is what ignites this chain reaction, any event that causes a small increase in temperature, such as an increase in solar activity, an El Nino, etc., should produce the same thermal runaway in global temperature. This has never happened in the entire historical climate record, even though temperatures have been much higher than today.

The "consensus" on the UN's IPCC rely solely on these failed computer models for their predictions of catastrophic warming with a doubling of the trace element carbon dioxide in the atmosphere. Erroneous simulations provide the gospel that demands mandatory reductions in greenhouse gas emissions and energy use by industrialized nations.

Global warming hysteria is based on projections of future climate by computer models that use free parameters (fudge factors) assigned to the unknowns in the black box of ignorance. The great mathematician, John von Neumann, once said: "If you allow me four free parameters I can build a mathematical model that describes what an elephant can do. With a fifth free parameter, the model will forecast that the elephant will fly."

The climate models used by the IPCC contain hundreds of free parameters. Man-made catastrophic global warming is an elephant that can fly.

FOUR

WATER

Water in its various forms (solid, liquid, and gas) is the most important ingredient in Earth's climate system, but it is the element that climate modelers know least about. Carbon dioxide possesses a warming characteristic through the greenhouse effect, but water possesses both warming and cooling properties through its absorption, reflection, transmission and heat-transfer characteristics. Climate modelers assign to water a positive feedback to carbon dioxide's warming characteristic, which amounts to a thermal avalanche designation for water that produces the catastrophic warming scenarios of computer simulations. What is the truth about water's influence on Earth's climate?

It is claimed by the IPCC that a doubling of CO_2 in the atmosphere from the pre-Industrial Age level of 0.028 percent will have catastrophic consequences due to global warming produced by the greenhouse effect. The concentration of water in the atmosphere in the form of water vapor, droplets, and clouds ranges from near zero percent to 4 percent and accounts for 90–95 percent of Earth's natural greenhouse effect. Hence, the concentration of water, the dominant greenhouse gas, exhibits a normal range of variation up to one hundred times greater than CO_2, yet there is no runaway global warming. In addition, the changes in water content of air (humidity) on a daily basis produce a much greater change in temperature from water's greenhouse effect than the entire increase in CO_2 over 150 years.

Why hasn't catastrophic warming been observed from the much

stronger greenhouse effect of water? The answer: water is not just a greenhouse gas. Water molecules have cooling properties that carbon dioxide does not. Evaporation transfers the heat of vaporization to the atmosphere, cooling the surface; condensation in the atmosphere provides cloud cover protection from the Sun's rays; precipitation provides downpours that terminate heat waves; and oceans of water molecules moderate the Earth's temperature extremes.

Furthermore, in 2001 NASA and Massachusetts Institute of Technology scientists discovered a safety valve for stabilizing Earth's temperature. When ocean temperature is above 82 degrees, a heat vent is created that allows heat to escape to outer space. It might be analogous to the updraft of a hurricane but without the cyclonic winds.

Recently, Roy Spencer has found another negative feedback from clouds in contradiction to climate models. Evidence from satellites reveals a decrease in high altitude cirrus clouds as the tropic atmosphere warms, allowing more infrared radiation to escape to outer space. Climate models attribute a positive feedback to cirrus clouds to amplify warming by CO_2.

Heat vents are ignored in the computer simulations used by the IPCC and the positive feedback assigned to clouds is contradicted by observations in the real world.

The process of evaporation, condensation, and precipitation of water molecules results in cooling of the Earth's surface and the formation of clouds, with an additional cooling provided by precipitation which removes the dominant greenhouse gas from the atmosphere.

The process constitutes a natural thermostat that controls the Earth's temperature and stabilizes the climate, regardless of the amount of CO_2 in the atmosphere.

The removal of the dominant greenhouse gas from the atmosphere by precipitation prompts one final tribute to the miraculous water molecule. When it rains, it doesn't rain carbon dioxide. Or does it? How much carbon dioxide is in a raindrop? It is not zero. Just as CO_2 is dissolved in the oceans, so too is CO_2 absorbed by water droplets in the atmosphere—the colder the droplet the greater the absorption of CO_2. The atmosphere doesn't rain carbon dioxide, but it does rain water containing carbon dioxide.

The water molecule may be the best defense against carbon emissions by humans, but the IPCC is silent on the cleansing of CO_2 from the atmosphere by the natural process of precipitation.

FIVE

THE UNITED NATIONS INTERGOVERNMENTAL PANEL ON CLIMATE CHANGE (IPCC)

A political organization, the United Nations Intergovernmental Panel on Climate Change (IPCC), has been anointed by global warming alarmists as the official scientific authority on global warming. This needs repeating: The IPCC is a political, not scientific, organization dominated and controlled by political, not scientific, appointees whose reports are dictated and written by governments, not scientists.

The only part of each IPCC report that is read or quoted is the Summary for Policymakers, a document often different from the underlying report. According to IPCC panel member Richard Lindzen of MIT, "The Summary for Policymakers represents a consensus of government representatives, not scientists. The resulting document has a strong tendency to disguise uncertainty, and conjures up some scary scenarios for which there is no evidence." Those are the restrained words of a member of the IPCC.

A revealing portrait of the IPCC is provided by just a few examples of the blunders contained in the reports of the IPCC:

1. The following statement was added to the Summary for Policymakers of the Second Report of the IPCC in 1995: "The balance of evidence suggests a discernible human influence on global climate." There was no scientific evidence in the report to support this claim.

2. In the Third Report of 2001, the IPCC adopted the so-called hockey stick of global temperature, claiming that the twentieth century was the warmest in the last one thousand years. The hockey stick erased from the climate record the Medieval Warm Period from AD 800 to 1300 and the Little Ice Age from AD 1300 to 1850. This "smoking gun" imploded when three independent studies proved the hockey stick to be a fraud.

3. The hockey stick was withdrawn from the Fourth Report of 2007. Scientific integrity required an explanation for the withdrawal and an acknowledgement of the hockey stick error. None was forthcoming. The inclusion of the hockey stick in the 2001 report was not an innocent mistake. The hockey stick replaced a thoroughly documented graph of global temperature appearing in the 1995 report that showed the Medieval Warm Period that was warmer than today. By erasing the Medieval Warm Period from the climate record, the IPCC could claim that the twentieth century was the warmest in the last one thousand years and could suggest that man was responsible for climate change. Adoption of the hockey stick constituted a revision of climate history and a deliberate falsification of the climate record.

4. To match the fraudulent hockey stick of global temperature, the IPCC fabricated a hockey stick of atmospheric CO_2. The fabrication involved ignoring "inconvenient" ice core data, rejecting 175 confirmed scientific studies with ninety thousand highly accurate direct measurements of atmospheric CO_2, and then manipulating the biased selection of data to fit the blade to the stick. Rejecting evidence that "does not fit the preconceived idea of man-made global warming" has been called "the greatest scientific scandal of our time." This is the origin of the IPCC's false claim that present levels of atmospheric CO_2 are the highest in the last one hundred

thousand years.

5. The official global temperature record of the IPCC from 1860 to the present shows an abrupt increase starting in 1990, leading to the claim that the 1990s was the hottest decade on record. The increase coincided with the collapse of the Soviet Union in 1989 and the closing of thousands of weather stations. The hottest decade is an illusion created by the IPCC by the elimination of thermometer readings from frigid Siberia and other cold regions.

6. Based on the IPCC's official temperature record, the year 1998 is claimed to be the hottest year on record. The claim is false. NASA's Goddard Institute for Space Studies has corrected data errors that changed the warmest year from 1998 to 1934. The warmest year on record can no longer be blamed on man-made greenhouse gases.

7. A major error in the official global temperature record of the IPCC is due to the "urban heat island" effect in which weather stations located in and around cities record waste heat generated in the city, not global warming due to greenhouse gases in the atmosphere. Ross McKitrick and Patrick Michaels have demonstrated recently that the urban heat island effect and other nonclimate—related factors affecting weather station data have resulted in an overstatement of the 1980–2002 global average temperature trend by approximately a factor of two. This forces a huge downward adjustment in all predictions of future climate, but this adjustment has not been made.

8. The computer simulations of climate used by the IPCC to forecast future climate fail to replicate climate in the last century. Therefore, they are incapable of predicting climate in the future and should be discarded for failing the fundamental test for all climate models.

9. The IPCC completely misrepresents the paleoclimate record over the last six hundred and fifty thousand years, claiming that warm periods were caused by increasing levels of carbon dioxide in the atmosphere when, in fact, increasing levels of CO_2 were caused by warming of the Earth from natural causes, which includes cyclical variations in Earth's orbit about the Sun.

10. The Summary for Policymakers is not a scientific document. It is written by bureaucrats, approved line by line by the governments of the nations of the UN, and frequently contradicts the information in the body of the report. The 2007 Summary was written by fifty-two political scientists selected by the IPCC. The so-called consensus of scientists of the IPCC, touted by global warming alarmists, is a consensus of bureaucrats, not scientists.

11. The IPCC claims that the warming in the last century was due to a progressive increase in atmospheric carbon dioxide since the beginning of the Industrial Age and is higher now than at any time in the last one hundred thousand years. Ernst-Georg Beck has demonstrated that carbon dioxide levels have been much higher than today—440 parts per million (ppm) in 1820 and 1940 compared with 380 ppm today. These higher levels cannot be attributed to the burning of fossil fuels by humans and they did not produce catastrophic warming of planet Earth. This finding proves that the last thread of evidence used by the IPCC is also wrong, and the case for global warming being caused by carbon dioxide in the atmosphere, whether from natural or man-made emissions, has collapsed.

12. The Summary for Policymakers of the 2007 IPCC report concludes that it is "very likely" that humans are to blame for global warming—an admission that there is no scientific evidence to support the claim. In science, "very likely" means "a guess without proof," "a suggestion without evidence to back it up."

The reports of the IPCC provide a permanent record of misrepresentation, erroneous data, deceit, scientific fraud, and political corruption of science. These are the corrupt practices that have been used to promote the global warming scam. In today's world, they are rewarded with a Nobel Peace Prize.

SIX

GLOBAL WARMING MYTHS

We've all heard the barrage of claims, broadcast in rapid-fire fashion to prevent individual challenge. The claims must be accepted as a matter of faith because they are obvious, exempt from scientific debate: man-made global warming is causing melting of polar ice caps, disappearance of glaciers, rising sea levels, flooding, droughts, hurricanes and tornados, mass extinction of species, a halt to ocean circulation, glaciation of Europe...you name it, man-made global warming is the cause.

This section examines each claim and describes the scientific evidence and scientific laws that govern the validity of each claim. One, and only one, alarmist claim survives this scrutiny.

MYTH #1:

The United States is the world's leading contributor of carbon dioxide to the atmosphere.

REALITY:

The United States is a leading emitter of carbon dioxide, but it is also, with Canada, the world's leading absorber of carbon dioxide from the atmosphere. According to research by the National Oceanic and Atmospheric Administration, published in the journal Science in 1998, North America is a sink for carbon dioxide. More carbon is removed from the atmosphere (almost 2 billion tons annually) than is generated by burning fossil fuels (1.5 billion tons annually). Carbon is being soaked up by the regrowth of plants and vegetation on abandoned farmland and previously logged forests.

MYTH #2:

The industrialized nations of the world must reduce carbon emissions by 80 percent below present levels to halt global warming.

REALITY:

This is the claim being made by United Nations Intergovernmental Panel on Climate Change (IPCC) extremists as the basis for Kyoto II that lies on the horizon when Kyoto I expires in 2012. The truth is that human activity contributes only about 3 percent of the carbon dioxide that enters the atmosphere every year. The remaining 97 percent is naturally occurring due to decaying vegetation, release of CO_2 from warming oceans, etc. If every nation on Earth (not just the industrialized nations) adopted a mandate to reduce carbon emissions by 80 percent below present levels, emissions to the atmosphere would be reduced by a miniscule 1 percent, resulting in an undetectable reduction in global warming due to CO_2. And there is no scientific evidence yet that carbon dioxide is responsible for any of the 1°F of warming in the last century.

The reduction would constitute an enormously costly and disruptive exercise in futility.

MYTH #3:

An increase of carbon dioxide in the atmosphere will produce catastrophic global warming.

REALITY:

It is not carbon dioxide but the inclusion of the
water molecule in mysterious and unjustifiable ways that
produces the catastrophic scenarios of computer models. According
to these models, an increase of carbon dioxide in the atmosphere
will produce a slight warming of the Earth's surface that increases
evaporation of water into the atmosphere. The increased water is
assumed to exert a positive feedback that amplifies the warming
due to CO_2 by a factor of 2.7 (a factor that is changed according
to the result desired). The feedback figure is a fudge factor that
reflects ignorance of the many ways that water influences climate,
including whether the feedback is positive or negative. A negative
feedback would indicate the stabilizing effect of water vapor on
Earth's climate with no catastrophic warming due to the greenhouse
effect, regardless of the CO_2 concentration in the atmosphere. Since
the carbon dioxide claim is dependent on unproven assumptions
about the role of water vapor, the carbon dioxide claim by the IPCC
is not credible.

It was shown earlier in section 4 that water vapor, the dominant
greenhouse gas, behaves as the thermostat on
Earth's temperature through the mechanisms of evaporation,
condensation and precipitation, irrespective of the level of CO_2 in
the atmosphere.

The most powerful evidence that catastrophic global warming
is a myth is provided by the historical climate record. As discussed
in Myth #29, levels of atmospheric CO_2 more than 15 times higher
than today did not produce global warming. Throughout the
climate history of Earth, and as recently as 1940, CO_2 levels have
been much higher than today with no heating attributed to CO_2.

Finally, Myth #28 describes how the laws of physics prohibit
catastrophic warming by atmospheric CO_2.

History and the laws of physics prove that the IPCC and its

climate modelers are wrong.

MYTH #4:

Warming of the Earth by greenhouse gases will have catastrophic consequences.

REALITY:

In the age of terrorism and the possibility of nuclear weapons in the hands of terrorists, it is claimed by some that the greatest threat to civilization is global warming and climate change. Greenhouse gases are demonized and carbon dioxide, the lifeblood of a green planet, is redefined as a pollutant by five scientifically challenged liberal activists on the U.S. Supreme Court.

Before being paralyzed by fear, consider this: If the Earth were not warmed by greenhouse gases, the Earth would be a very cold place to live. Instead of the present global average temperature of a pleasant 15°C (59°F), the average temperature would be a frigid -18°C (0°F).

The Earth warmed a modest 1°F in the last century, but there is no scientific evidence that any of this warming was caused by CO_2, while there is extensive evidence that it was not caused by CO_2. In the historical climate record over the last 650,000 years there is no evidence that warm periods were caused by CO_2 in the atmosphere.

The more recent climate record provides insight on the consequences of both a warmer and a colder planet. The Medieval Warm Period (or Medieval Climate Optimum) from AD 900 to 1300 was as much as 2°F warmer than today. The shoreline of Greenland turned green and was settled by Eric the Red, and civilization prospered from a more stable climate, longer growing seasons, and agricultural abundance. The period following the Medieval Warm Period from AD 1300 to 1850 is known as the Little Ice Age. A climate about 2°F cooler than today brought crop failure and mass starvation, floods that killed hundreds of thousands, and epidemics of bubonic plague and typhus that killed 30 million in Europe and 40 million in Africa. Today's alarmists have the consequences of climate change exactly backward.

At the current rate of increase of 1°F per century, world temperatures will reach those of the Medieval Warm Period in two hundred years. Far from being a catastrophe, the world can look forward to a return to a climate optimum over the next two centuries.

MYTH #5:

The graphs of the rise in carbon dioxide and the rise in temperature over the last 650,000 years showed "an exact fit" (Al Gore in his movie An Inconvenient Truth).

REALITY:

When the two graphs are superimposed on one another, an astounding conclusion is drawn: the changes in temperature precede the changes in carbon dioxide by 800–2000 years. In other words, warm periods of the past were not caused by carbon dioxide in the atmosphere, but rather, warming of the Earth generated carbon dioxide in the atmosphere.

The explanation lies with the oceans, which hold about 50 times more CO_2 than the atmosphere. The amount of carbon dioxide dissolved as carbonates in the oceans depends on ocean temperature, not air temperature. When oceans are warmed by solar irradiation, they release some of the carbon dioxide to the atmosphere, similar to a can of soda losing its carbonation as it warms up. If ocean temperature were to increase from 15°C (59°F) to 20°C (68°F), 20 percent of the stored carbon dioxide would be released to the atmosphere. In other words, the entire increase of atmospheric CO_2 in the last century would be accounted for by a 1°F increase in ocean temperature. But oceans are vast and deep.

Warming of the oceans and release of carbon dioxide is delayed by 800–2000 years from the warming of the Earth and its atmosphere. This explains why Earth's temperature changes before carbon dioxide appears in the atmosphere.

The greenhouse global warming theory has it backward. It is the warming of the Earth and Earth's oceans that causes the increase of CO_2 in the atmosphere and not the reverse.

MYTH #6:

The 1°F warming of Earth's climate during the last century was caused by global warming due to greenhouse gases in the atmosphere.

REALITY:

More than half of the increase in temperature occurred before 1940—before any significant increase of CO_2 in the atmosphere. The Earth cooled from 1940 to the 1970s, when CO_2 in the atmosphere increased most rapidly. The Earth has warmed since 1980, but if the warming were due to greenhouse gases, theory requires that the temperature of the lower troposphere (below ~ 30,000 feet) should increase faster than the temperature at the surface. Satellite data since 1979 and weather balloon measurements since 1958 show virtually no increase.

Furthermore, global warming in the last century was not global. Satellite and balloon data reveal that the tropics and the southern hemisphere cooled, while in the northern hemisphere, some places warmed while others cooled, even though the concentration of CO_2 in the atmosphere was the same everywhere.

There is no signal of a human contribution to global warming in the twentieth century.

MYTH #7:

The polar ice caps are melting due to global warming.

REALITY:

The western part of the Arctic has been warming, but the eastern part has been cooling since the 1930s. A small part of Antarctica (the West Antarctic ice sheet) has been warming, while most of Antarctica (97 percent) has been cooling, and growing, for over forty years. Since 90 percent of the world's ice is in Antarctica, there is no loss of ice from melting of the polar ice caps.

Much alarmist rhetoric is heard about melting sea ice in the Arctic. Recently, scientists from Woods Hole Oceanographic Institution discovered that under the sea ice lies the largest volcanic chain in the world, with pyroclastic deposits on the sea floor created by explosive eruptions of carbon dioxide.

Since oceans are warmed by the Sun and cannot be warmed by the greenhouse effect of carbon dioxide in the atmosphere (see Myth #15), alarmist scientists may have found a legitimate mechanism by which carbon dioxide can melt sea ice—explosive volcanic eruptions of carbon dioxide from beneath the sea floor. Computer modelers should look down instead of up.

What about the alarmists' claim that an ice shelf breaking off from the West Antarctic ice sheet is proof of global warming? In 2008, a research vessel discovered an active volcano with fresh lava flow located in the vicinity of a collapsed ice shelf. Is the West Antarctic ice sheet immune to geothermal heating of seawater by an active volcano?

MYTH # 8:

Glaciers are melting because of global warming by greenhouse gases.

REALITY:

Glaciers began to retreat when the world emerged from the Little Ice Age around 1850. Half of the length reduction occurred before 1900—before the first automobile assembly line. Three-fourths of the reduction had occurred before 1950, when atmospheric CO_2 had increased only 20 percent from the level in 1900. The natural warming of the Earth that brought an end to the Little Ice Age is responsible for the retreat of glaciers, not greenhouse gases in the atmosphere.

MYTH # 9:

Calving of glaciers is caused by global warming.

REALITY:

Video of a calving glacier is the media's favorite "proof" of global warming. Glaciers and ice shelves are flowing rivers of ice. When enough ice accumulates in the overhang into the sea, it falls of its own weight. Contrary to the Al Gore movie, "calving" is caused by the force of gravity, not by greenhouse gases in the atmosphere.

MYTH #10:

The snows of Mt. Kilimanjaro are melting because of global warming.

REALITY:

The snows are disappearing due to decades-long lack of moisture. No moisture, no snow; no replenishment of the snow on Kilimanjaro. Furthermore, the satellite record shows the Kilimanjaro region has been cooling since the record began in 1979.

MYTH #11:

A sea level rise of up to 20 feet will be caused by melting of either West Antarctica or Greenland in the near future (Al Gore).

REALITY:

A small part of Antarctica (West Antarctica) has been warming but most of Antarctica (97 percent) has been cooling for over forty years. The accumulation of ice over most of Antarctica more than compensates for the loss of ice in West Antarctica and, in fact, the growing ice sheet is lowering sea level.

Greenland has been cooling since the 1930s and gaining in ice thickness. Most of Greenland's ice surface is at an altitude over a mile high at subzero temperatures even in summer. Only Al Gore believes that Greenland's glaciers will melt in year-round subzero temperatures.

Alarmist James Hansen, an advisor to Gore, is the source of Gore's claim that Greenland's glaciers will slide into the sea. A climate modeler, Hansen has a model for the collapse of a glacier whereby an ice sheet slides downhill on a base lubricated by increasing amounts of meltwater produced by global warming. Glaciers over two miles thick at subzero temperatures do not melt from the surface down nor do they flow on a lubricated base. They flow by creep resulting from the force of gravity acting on the mass of accumulated ice. Hansen is uninformed about the genesis and dynamics of glaciers, but the false model is appealing to television programs promoting catastrophic warming.

In November 1987, Hansen made the apocalyptic prediction

that "the global warming predicted in the next 20 years will make the Earth warmer than it has been in the past 100,000 years." Being wrong is the hallmark of climate alarmists.

MYTH #12:

Polar bears are drowning from swimming long distances to find ice (Al Gore).

REALITY:

It is now known that the four polar bears in Al Gore's film drowned because of a severe storm, not because of loss of pack ice. The film also used a computer-generated lonely polar bear to reinforce the message that the polar bear is on the verge of extinction due to global warming. On the contrary, the Arctic polar bear population has increased from five thousand to more than twenty thousand in the last fifty years. According to the World Wildlife Fund, there were twenty-two thousand polar bears in twenty distinct populations across the Arctic in 2001. A map of the regions where populations were changing shows that in Arctic regions where the temperature is increasing, the polar bear population is increasing; in regions where temperatures are in decline, the polar bear population is in decline. The Arctic polar bear population is thriving with global warming.

Concerning the disappearing sea ice, Canada's Department of Fisheries and Oceans finds that "changes in wind patterns lead to large-scale redistributions of ice rather than an overall decline. Global warming appears to play a minor role in changes to Arctic sea ice."

MYTH #13:

The 1990s was the hottest decade in history and the ten hottest years ever measured all occurred in the last fourteen years (Al Gore).

REALITY:

A Canadian researcher, Ross McKitrick, has made the remarkable discovery that the hottest decade is correlated with the collapse of the Soviet Union in 1989 and the closing of thousands of the world's weather stations—from twelve thousand stations in 1988 to five thousand stations operating today. The elimination of thermometer readings from frigid Siberia and other cold regions created the illusion that the 1990s was the hottest decade on record.

Furthermore, McKitrick and Patrick Michaels have demonstrated recently that the surface temperature data used by the IPCC are contaminated by the urban heat island effect and other factors affecting weather station readings. These nonclimate effects lead to an overstatement of the 1980–2002 global average temperature trend by about a factor of two.

The IPCC's official temperature record is contaminated by erroneous weather station data since 1980 and is biased by the absence of readings from cold regions since 1989. These errors are magnified when the official temperature record is incorporated into computer models for projections of future climate.

MYTH #14:

The year 1998 was the hottest year on record.

REALITY:

Wrong again. NASA's Goddard Institute for Space Studies has corrected data errors that changed the warmest year from 1998 to

1934. The warmest year on record can no longer be blamed on greenhouse gases. Also, 1998 experienced a thermal spike caused by El Nino, an ocean and atmospheric phenomenon that boosts sea surface temperatures all over the Pacific Ocean and is unrelated to the greenhouse effect.

MYTH #15:

Global warming will increase the temperature of the world's oceans.

REALITY:

The ocean is warmed by the Sun, not by the air above it. Solar radiation penetrates the ocean to a depth of about 100 meters. But infrared radiation from the greenhouse effect penetrates to a depth of only a few millimeters. It is within these few millimeters that evaporation takes place, transferring water molecules carrying the latent heat of evaporation to the atmosphere.

Furthermore, since warm water does not sink, a warm surface layer a few millimeters thick cannot possibly warm a cold deep ocean.

MYTH #16:

Hurricane Katrina was caused by global warming (Al Gore) and hurricanes will increase in intensity and frequency with the buildup of greenhouse gases in the atmosphere (IPCC).

REALITY:

Hurricane seasons come in cycles—periods of twenty-five to forty years that are very active and twenty-five to forty years that are very quiet. The most active hurricane decade on record was 1941–1950, before atmospheric carbon dioxide had increased appreciably. During the forty-year period 1961–2000, both the number and the intensity of hurricanes striking the U.S. decreased sharply—a period when carbon emissions increased most rapidly. According to the historical cyclical pattern, the U.S. is in a twenty-five-to-forty-year period of active hurricanes, but not because of global warming.

A threshold surface water temperature of 81°F permits a hurricane to form; it does not cause a hurricane to form, because a hurricane is an atmospheric, not a surface phenomenon. The development of a hurricane requires a corridor of low pressure, circulating wind patterns, and a supply of warm moisture-laden air along its entire trajectory. The establishment of these atmospheric conditions determines the strength and frequency of hurricanes, not sea surface temperature or global warming.

A possible influence of greenhouse gases on hurricanes may be found in the troposphere (the lower atmosphere up to thirty thousand feet)—where carbon dioxide absorbs heat radiated from the Earth's surface. The energy in the warmed troposphere creates vertical wind shear (a difference in wind speed and direction at different altitudes) that cuts off the tops of hurricanes by dissipating the heat of rising air over a larger area. Hence, global warming by the greenhouse effect may decrease, not increase, the intensity and frequency of hurricanes, and may explain the two consecutive very quiet hurricane years of 2006 and 2007.

MYTH #17:

Severe weather events will increase as carbon dioxide levels rise.

REALITY:

The claim of more extreme weather events in a warmer world is based on the simplistic view that more heat equals more evaporation equals more rain. But rain is normal, and essential. It is not an extreme weather event. Severe storms arise from the parameters that move air masses rapidly: large gradients in air temperature and pressure. The origin of extreme weather events is the difference in temperature between the polar regions and the tropics. The larger the temperature difference between the equator and the poles, the greater the power given to the winds, waves, and ocean currents— and to storms. But greenhouse gas theory predicts a warming that increases temperatures more in winter than in summer, and more in the polar regions than in the tropics, reducing the temperature difference between the poles and the equator. This means milder and fewer severe storms in a warmer world, contrary to the prediction of climate models.

Weather in most of the world is governed by the movement of cold air from the polar regions. Just as air does not halt the movement of water along a surface, so warm air cannot halt the flow of more dense cold air along Earth's surface. When dense cold air, flowing unimpeded except for mountains, encounters warm moist air from the tropics, storms and extreme weather events are created. The colder the air in the polar regions, the more frequent and more extreme the weather events. A warming of the atmosphere by greenhouse gases, occurring preferentially in the polar regions, would raise the temperature of cold polar air and weaken the strength and storm creating potential of these polar air masses. Unfortunately, the polar ice caps are not melting (see Myth #7) and the atmosphere is not being warmed by CO_2 (see Myth #6). The computer models are not working. In order to reduce severe weather events, another method will have to be found to warm the polar regions to reduce the temperature difference between the polar regions and the tropics. CO_2 in the atmosphere won't do it.

A reliable forecast of weather in a warmer world is revealed by the Medieval Warm Period (900 1300 A.D.), when temperatures were warmer than today and the climate was stable, and the Little Ice Age (1300 1850 A.D.), characterized by an unstable climate, short growing seasons, reduced harvests, mass starvation, catastrophic rains and storm surges.

MYTH #18:

Low-lying Pacific atolls are being inundated because of anthropogenic (man-made) global warming and have already been evacuated (Al Gore).

REALITY:

According to the international Sea Level Commission, sea level around the Maldive Islands in the Indian Ocean was higher between 1900 and 1970 than today, and that sea level has fallen by 8–12 inches since 1970, in the middle of a warm period.

Since 1993, satellite radars have found that sea levels around Tuvalu in the Pacific Ocean have dropped by four inches over a decade, and Tuvalu is located in a region where sea level has declined for nearly fifty years. No one has been evacuated from Tuvalu. According to an environmental official on Tuvalu, "People are telling all these lies because Tuvalu is being used for the issue of climate change."

MYTH #19:

Global warming will increase the severity and frequency of drought (IPCC).

REALITY:

The IPCC selected the midwestern U.S. to predict that a doubling of greenhouse gas concentrations will result in a 20 percent decrease in soil moisture and a 10 percent decrease in rainfall during the summer months, increasing the severity and frequency of drought. The basis for the claim is simply this:

Global warming = more evaporation = less soil moisture = more drought

But an accurate statement would also state:

Global warming = more evaporation = more rain = less drought

The question becomes this: Does evaporation that depletes soil moisture exceed evaporation that replenishes soil moisture through rainfall? The answer is known. During the buildup of greenhouse gases over the twentieth century, precipitation records show an increase in precipitation, completely contrary to the IPCC prediction.

Why are the climate modelers wrong? There are two reasons. First, evaporation that depletes soil moisture produces rain somewhere. The moisture does not disappear. Second, evaporation from 70 percent of the Earth's surface—the oceans—produces rain that does not deplete soil moisture.

MYTH #20:

Global warming will lead to plant and animal extinction.

REALITY:

Each year we lose about forty thousand species. How do we know this? Al Gore says so in his book Earth in the Balance. A famous Harvard biologist E.O. Wilson places the figure of lost species at between twenty-seven thousand and one hundred thousand per year. Another icon of environmental fiction, Professor Paul Ehrlich, stated in 1981 that we lose two hundred and fifty thousand species every year, that half of Earth's species will be gone by the year 2000 and all species gone by 2010–2125.

How many species inhabit the Earth? No one knows. Estimates

range from 10 to 80 million, but only about 1.6 million have been identified to date. With such lack of knowledge about the number and nature of existing species, how do biologists justify their claims as to the number of species and the number going extinct? They don't. They say the burden of proof is on the disbelievers. If we don't believe there are 80 million species and forty thousand are becoming extinct every year, go out into the jungles and prove it. They admit they have no evidence to support the claim of forty thousand extinctions each year, but we must do everything to halt this "human-caused biotic holocaust."

Global warming now provides a convenient vehicle to resurrect and incorporate these discredited claims of species extinction into a new human-caused environmental catastrophe. One scenario of extinction due to global warming is provided by a British ecologist, Chris Thomas. He asserts that an increase in Earth's temperature of 0.8°C in the next fifty years will cause the extinction of 20 percent of the world's species, perhaps 1 million of them. But Earth's temperature has already increased 0.6°C over the past 150 years. How many species died out because of that temperature increase? None. If a warming planet will cause extinction of any species, that species is already extinct from previous periods that were warmer than today: the Medieval Warm Period (eight hundred years ago), the Holocene Climate Optimum (about seven thousand years ago and lasting three thousand years) and the last interglacial period (one hundred and twenty thousand years ago).

The poster child for threatened and endangered species and species extinction is the polar bear. Global warming is melting the pack ice needed by polar bears to hunt seals, the main food source. Al Gore claims they are already drowning from having to swim long distances.

In reality, the four bears perished in a storm. And the polar bear that died of starvation because of global warming? The bear had attacked a colony of walruses and was gored to death.

Despite the false claims of Al Gore and the deceit of the media, the polar bear is not only not on the verge of extinction but is thriving.

To exist on planet Earth, a species has found a habitat and acquired the capability to adapt to large and abrupt changes in local climate. A species that thrives in New Jersey has adapted to a temperature change of as much as 40°F within twenty-four hours (the daily high and low) and a seasonal temperature change from 0° to 100°F (the yearly high and low). The claim that a change in the yearly temperature range of a few degrees, from 0°-100°F to 2°-102°F over the time span of one hundred years, will cause a species to become extinct is absurd.

Unless global warming can cause an asteroid to impact the Earth, the greatest threats to species survival remain competition from other species, natural predators, pests and diseases, and the best safeguard against these threats is man.

MYTH #21:

Global warming will expand the area for tropical diseases such as malaria (IPCC).

REALITY:

The claim by the IPCC is based on the false notion that malaria is only a disease of the tropics and, therefore, a disease associated with tropical temperatures. The IPCC conceals the well-known fact that throughout the Little Ice Age, malaria was a major epidemic disease in Europe and extended far into the Arctic Circle. In Russia during the 1920s, 650,000 died from the mosquito-borne disease. Malaria remains endemic in Siberia today.

Malaria is controlled by eradicating mosquitoes and their breeding grounds, not by controlling air temperature. "It's tires, not global warming" that accounts for the spread of mosquitoes, according to Professor Paul Reiter of the Pasteur Institute. If warmer air was the determining factor in expanding the habitat for mosquitoes, the reemergence of malaria would be seen already in the U.S. and other areas previously afflicted, since the Earth has been warming for 150 years since the end of the Little Ice Age.

The IPCC erroneously claims that mosquitoes survive only at temperatures above 16°C (61°F). Members of the IPCC panel should be required to provide proof of their claim by visiting the caribou herds in the cold tundra of the Arctic in spring. Humans could be bled to death by mosquitoes that the IPCC says do not exist.

If the concern about tropical diseases were genuine, the IPCC would support eliminating the ban on DDT, a ban enacted under pressure from environmental extremists that condemned over 1 million people in Africa and Asia to death from malaria every year.

MYTH #22:

Higher temperatures from global warming will increase human death rates.

REALITY:

There are certainly deaths due to heat waves. But there are also deaths due to cold waves. From 1979 to 1997, extreme cold killed twice as many Americans as heat waves, according to Indur Goklany of the U.S. Department of the Interior. Cold spells are twice as dangerous to our health as hot weather.

Moreover, global warming would raise minimum winter temperatures significantly more that it would raise maximum summer temperatures. So today's higher death rate in winter would be reduced much more than any increase in the death rate in summer, and the overall human death rate will decline with global warming.

MYTH #23:

Climate change will bring starvation to the developing world.

REALITY:

As discussed in the next section on the benefits of CO_2, a warmer world with higher CO_2 in the atmosphere means longer growing seasons, enhanced plant growth and a boon for agriculture. Historically, global cooling has been the harbinger of starvation, such as the Great Famine of AD 1315 during the Little Ice Age.

Limiting economic growth by restricting access to energy is certain to bring economic recession to developed countries and keep undeveloped countries in poverty and hunger.

MYTH #24:

A warmer world will lead to reduced world food production.

REALITY:

The deceit here is the failure to mention the alleged cause of the warming: a higher atmospheric concentration of carbon dioxide. Carbon dioxide is the essential ingredient for photosynthesis, the process by which plants produce the carbohydrates of plant fiber for plant growth. Increased CO_2 in the atmosphere not only fertilizes plants and increases crop yields but enables them to use water more efficiently.

What is the optimum concentration of atmospheric carbon dioxide for life on planet Earth? Alarmists want a return to the preindustrial level of 280 ppm, claiming that the increase to 380 ppm is due to the burning of fossil fuels by humans and any increase due to humans is bad for the planet. The claim is refuted in Myths 5, 6, and 29.

In the climatological history of planet Earth, the concentration has been as low as 180 ppm—during ice ages of the last 650,000 years. If there were no CO_2 in the atmosphere, all life on Earth would cease to exist. Contrary to the claims of alarmists, science reveals that, for plant growth and food production, the concentration of atmospheric CO_2 is too low, not too high.

In 1997, the U.S. Department of Agriculture found that an increase of CO_2 in the atmosphere from 200 ppm to the present level of 350 ppm increased wheat production by 48 percent under semi-drought conditions and 72 percent under watered conditions.

In 2002, an analysis of 159 peer-reviewed articles showed that increasing the CO_2 concentration by 150-450 ppm resulted in an average 20 percent increase in the growth of fruits, flowers, and seeds.

Another analysis of 279 published experiments revealed that increasing CO_2 to the possible eventual maximum of 600 ppm would increase plant growth 50 percent under normal conditions and 100 percent under stress such as drought.

So, not only has plant growth been enhanced by the 30 percent increase in CO_2 that has already taken place, but the enhancement in the future will be even greater. The evidence is conclusive that at the present level of 380 ppm of CO_2 in the atmosphere, the planet is experiencing a deficiency in an essential ingredient for food production.

The defining characteristics of greenhouse gas warming are that nights warm more than days, winters warm more than summers, cold regions warm more than the tropics, more evaporation and more rain. This means less frost damage, longer growing seasons, less drought, higher crop yields and a greater world food supply—and a greener planet.

MYTH #25:

Global warming will switch off the Gulf Stream and bring about glaciation (Al Gore).

REALITY:

The argument is made that freshwater, produced by the melting of Arctic and Greenland ice, will flow into the North Atlantic, lowering the salinity and density of ocean surface water and preventing it from sinking to the bottom as part of the thermohaline circulation pattern of the world's oceans. It is claimed that this will halt the flow of the warm waters of the Gulf Stream and bring cold weather—and even glaciation—to Europe.

Problem 1: Half of the Arctic ice sheet melts every summer. This addition of freshwater will lower the salinity and turn off the Gulf Stream every summer. Cold weather and glaciation of Europe should happen every year, in summer!

Problem 2: If global warming has melted the ice of the Arctic and Greenland, the same warm atmosphere cannot freeze the ice to produce glaciation.

It has been said by MIT Professor Karl Wunsch that the only way for the Gulf Stream to shut down is for the Earth to stop rotating and for the wind to stop blowing. These two factors govern circulation of the Earth's oceans, not CO_2 in the atmosphere. Halting the Gulf Stream by means of global warming is a scientific impossibility.

The fable of the shutdown of the Gulf Stream was a feature of the disaster movie The Day after Tomorrow. Hollywood does not have to obey the laws of physics—nor do computer models of Earth's climate.

MYTH #26:

Coral reefs all over the world are being bleached because of global warming (Al Gore).

REALITY:

Bleaching is the normal reaction of the coral's system to sudden temperature changes, whether warmer or colder, and not an indication of the death of coral. In response to a temperature change, such as an El Nino warming of the entire Pacific, algae on the coral is ejected and subsequently replaced by a new strain of algae. Corals have adapted to seventeen glacial-interglacial temperature shifts in the last 2 million years, along with a sea level change of as much as four hundred feet since the last ice age.

MYTH #27:

The increase of CO_2 in the atmosphere from 280 ppm to 380 ppm in the 20th century is entirely due to the burning of fossil fuels by humans (IPCC).

REALITY:

The increase in atmospheric CO_2 in the last century was caused by the release of CO_2 by solar warming of ocean surface waters by 0.6°C (1°F), and the decay of land and marine vegetation. Less than 3 percent is due to the burning of fossil fuels by humans, a contribution that is smaller than the natural annual variability of atmospheric CO_2. The IPCC's claim is false.

What is the basis of the claim by the IPCC? The claim is based on a simple calculation of the rate of generation of CO_2 by the burning of fossil fuels multiplied by the "lifetime" that CO_2 remains in the atmosphere before it is absorbed by the oceans. The IPCC arbitrarily chooses a lifetime of up to two hundred years to make it appear that the human contribution matches the measured increase of CO_2 in the 20th century. There are more than three-dozen studies that prove that the lifetime is five to ten years. By creating a fictitious lifetime, the IPCC deliberately magnifies the true human contribution by at least a factor of twenty.

The implication for computer models is devastating. Since the computer models used by the IPCC use the fabricated lifetime that exaggerates the human contribution to atmospheric CO_2 by a factor of twenty, the projections of computer models are worthless and the panic over man-made global warming is groundless.

If there is a doubling of CO_2 in the atmosphere by the year 2100, it will be caused by oceans warmed by solar activity, not emissions produced by human activity.

MYTH #28:

A doubling of carbon dioxide in the atmosphere from 280 ppm to 560 ppm will double the global warming produced by carbon emissions.

REALITY:

A scientific fact suppressed by the IPCC is that a doubling of carbon dioxide in the atmosphere will not double the warming due to the greenhouse effect. The increase in warming will be negligible. The absorption characteristic of the CO_2 molecule reveals that the first 100 ppm of CO_2 in the atmosphere absorbs more than 95 percent of Earth's radiant energy that the molecule is capable of absorbing. The next 100 ppm cannot absorb the 95 percent that has already been absorbed; it can only absorb a portion of the remaining 5 percent. Similarly, each additional amount of CO_2 added to the atmosphere absorbs correspondingly less radiant heat from the surface and produces less warming by the greenhouse effect.

This saturation effect means that nearly all of the warming potential of CO_2 has been realized at an atmospheric concentration of less than 100 ppm. Concentrations higher than 100 ppm produce negligible warming, including the pre-industrial level of 280 ppm and the feared doubling level of 560 ppm. Atmospheric CO_2 is not capable of producing catastrophic global warming because the warming potential has been essentially exhausted.

Satellite measurements since 1979 show no change in near-surface atmospheric temperatures despite a 15 percent increase in atmospheric CO_2.

Higher concentrations of atmospheric CO_2 merely produce a greener, not warmer, planet.

MYTH # 29:

The IPCC claims that CO_2 levels today are higher than at any time in the last one hundred thousand years.

REALITY:

There exists an extensive scientific record of atmospheric CO_2 from earliest times up to the present. Extensive glaciation occurred about 400 million years ago when atmospheric carbon dioxide was as high as 6000 ppm. The planet was not incinerated by a level of CO_2 more than 15 times higher than today.

As Earth emerged from the last ice age eleven thousand years ago, the level increased from 180 ppm to 350 ppm, the same as today. About fifteen hundred years ago, around AD 500, the atmospheric CO_2 level exceeded 400 ppm.

More recently, a German scientist, Ernst-Georg Beck, discovered that levels of atmospheric CO_2 were much higher than today with levels of 440 ppm in 1820 and 1940, compared with 380 ppm today. Neither of these higher levels can be attributed to the burning of fossil fuels by humans. Most importantly, these higher levels did not produce global warming in the years following.

This remarkable finding further confirms that man-made global warming is a myth.

MYTH #30:

The safe upper limit for atmospheric carbon dioxide is no more than 350 parts per million.

REALITY:

In December 2007, alarmist James Hansen claimed that the safe upper limit for atmospheric CO_2 is no more than 350 ppm. Any higher level would cause Greenland's giant ice sheet to slide into the ocean, raising sea levels by 20 feet (the Al Gore claim in his movie; see Myth #11). The present level is already 380 ppm. Levels of 440 ppm were recorded in 1820 and 1940, and Greenland's glaciers survived.

MYTH #31:

The activity of the Sun cannot possibly explain the global warming of the last century (IPCC).

REALITY:

The polar ice cap is melting; the climate is the warmest it has been in more than a century. Doesn't this prove that humans are responsible for climate change? No. The planet described is Mars, not Earth. Mars does not have a greenhouse gas atmosphere and the Martians do not burn fossil fuels. But Mars has global warming. Mars and Earth have one thing in common—the Sun. Since it is the Sun that warms Mars, the Sun has also been warming the Earth.

While acknowledging in its 2007 report that the IPCC has very little scientific understanding of how the Sun influences Earth's climate, the IPCC states that the variation in solar radiance contributed only about 7 percent of the global warming contribution claimed for CO_2 in the last century. But it is not a variation in solar radiance that is most important; it is the far greater variation in solar magnetic activity that governs Earth's climate.

Unlike Mars, planet Earth has an atmosphere that amplifies variations in the Sun's activity. As discussed in section 12, solar magnetic activity, revealed by sunspots, governs the formation of cooling low-level clouds by modulating the intensity of cosmic rays impacting Earth's atmosphere. A variation in cloud cover of only a few percent is sufficient to change Earth's temperature by 1°C (2°F).

The Sun, through its influence on cosmic rays and clouds, can explain global warming (and cooling) of the last century. Carbon dioxide emissions do not.

MYTH #32:

The warming of the Earth since 1980 can only be explained by human-caused global warming.

REALITY:

This has become the last gasp of the IPCC and global warming alarmists. With the failure to uncover a shred of evidence to replace the fraudulent hockey sticks of global temperature and atmospheric CO_2 (see section 7), and the failure of computer models and the greenhouse gas theory to explain any aspect of climate change in the past, the alarmists and the IPCC have focused on the last few decades, claiming that only the production of carbon dioxide by humans can explain the increase in global temperature since 1980.

Once again, science is the enemy of the alarmists. Atmospheric CO_2 has continued to slowly increase since 1980, but global warming has stopped. There has been no warming for ten years, since 1998, and the entire increase in global temperature over the last century was wiped out in the last two years.

How can this be? The answer is that Earth's climate has always been governed by natural causes, not CO_2. The known record over hundreds of millions of years has shown that even 6000 ppm of

CO_2 in the atmosphere did not prevent glaciation, and that CO_2 has never been the cause of an increase in Earth's temperature.

What is the cause of the reversal in the global temperature trend? The end of global warming coincides with the cycles of solar activity. After an extraordinarily high level of solar activity that corresponded with the warming and cooling periods of the last century, solar activity is now in decline and decades of global cooling lie ahead. As described in section 12, low solar activity results in increasing cloud-cover shielding from the Sun's illumination and cooling of Earth's surface.

Cloud cover since the 1980s has been determined by both satellites and by a very unique method—by measuring "earthshine." Earthshine is the light reflected by the Earth's sunlit atmosphere toward the moon and reflected back to Earth by the lunar surface. In effect, the moon is used as a mirror to determine the amount of sunlight reflected by Earth's cloud cover.

The evidence confirms that the warming (and cooling) of the Earth since 1980 is consistent with solar activity and cloud formation, not CO_2 in the atmosphere.

TRUE CLAIM:

But the alarmists should be given credit when they make a true statement, supported by sound science, as in the following: More CO_2 in the atmosphere will make poison ivy and ragweed grow faster. Indeed, researchers at the Marine Biological Laboratory in Woods Hole, Massachusetts, have found that higher levels of carbon dioxide cause poison ivy vines to grow twice as much per year as they do now.

It is true, as the cherry-picking alarmists claim, that poison ivy and ragweed will enjoy the same benefit of enhanced growth from carbon dioxide fertilization as all other plants and food crops.

CONCLUSION

Since the enhanced growth of poison ivy and ragweed in a CO_2-enriched atmosphere is hardly a catastrophe, every claim of catastrophic consequences from man-made global warming is contradicted by existing scientific evidence.

But baseless claims are only part of the story. The alarmists' Bible on global warming consists of reports issued by the United Nations IPCC and Al Gore's book and movie An Inconvenient Truth. The foundation documents of the IPCC are fraudulent graphs of mean global temperature and atmospheric CO_2 (see section 7 on the Hockey Sticks) and computer simulations programmed with fictitious fudge factors to produce a predetermined political result: that humans are the cause of climate change (see section 3 on Computer Models).

A British magistrate has found at least nine false or unproven claims in Al Gore's movie and refused to approve its viewing in British schools unless alternate views were presented. According to Judge Michael Burton, students in more than thirty-five hundred British schools would have been subjected to unchallenged political indoctrination based on unproven assertions, false claims, alarmist propaganda, and "Armageddon scenarios not in line with scientific consensus." Note that Judge Burton was not ruling on the multitude of errors in the so-called scientific consensus of the IPCC. Informed viewers will recognize Gore's movie as Hollywood fantasy portrayed as scientific fact. The movie is designed in the belief that the audience is uninformed and can be persuaded with an emotional—not intellectual— appeal. It is presented by a hypocrite seeking to profit from carbon footprint guilt. The message delivered by Gore is this: If you want to save the planet, follow me and don't ask questions. Do as I say, not as I do."

SEVEN

THE HOCKEY STICKS

The object that will forever be identified with the global warming scandal is the hockey stick, or rather two hockey sticks—one for the hockey stick of global temperature over the last one thousand years, the other for the hockey stick of CO_2 in the atmosphere over the same period. As described briefly in section 5 on the IPCC, the hockey stick of global temperature was designed to show a nearly constant global temperature since AD 1000 until global temperature shot up dramatically (by 1°F) with the beginning of the industrial age around AD 1850.

To link the alleged increase in global temperature to the burning of fossil fuels in the industrial age, a second hockey stick had to be created showing a constant level of CO_2 in the atmosphere until AD 1850 and a sharp rise thereafter that would be blamed on the burning of fossil fuels.

Three independent studies found the hockey stick of global temperature to be a fraud: the first by Canadian researchers Ross McKitrick and Steven McIntyre; the second by a panel of the National Academy of Sciences; the third by a group commissioned by Congress led by Edward Wegman of George Mason University. The falsification of the global temperature record by the IPCC in its 2001 report was deliberate and premeditated, replacing a thoroughly documented graph of global temperature in its 1995 report showing the Medieval Warm Period warmer than today and that the planet was emerging from the Little Ice Age in 1850.

But the fraud in the hockey stick of global temperature pales in comparison to the fraud employed in the creation of the hockey stick of atmospheric CO_2. To create the handle of the hockey stick, the IPCC wanted to show that the level of atmospheric CO_2 had always been at about the level assigned to the preindustrial age, 280 ppm. Using ice core proxy data from the Antarctic, here is how they did it, according to Zbigniew Jaworowski, the world's foremost authority on ice cores: The ice core information was "plagued with improper manipulation of data, an arbitrary rejection of high readings from old ice, and an arbitrary rejection of low readings from young ice, simply because they did not fit the preconceived idea of man-made global warming. Ice cores that show levels of over 400 ppm as recently as AD 1700 and 420 ppm around AD 200 do not fit the preconceived idea of man-made global warming."

Even more incriminating are the tricks used to produce the blade of the CO_2 hockey stick. The IPCC used two different sets of data for the blade: an ice core record showing a rise from 280 ppm in AD 1700 before the Revolutionary War to 328 ppm in 1890, and a Mauna Loa Observatory record showing a steady rise from 315 ppm in 1958 to 380 ppm today. This leaves a gap in the record from 1890 to 1958, together with the inconvenient fact that the level of CO_2 was higher in 1890 than in 1958. So the "scientists" at the IPCC merely shifted the ice core data forward in time by eighty-three years to blend smoothly into the Mauna Loa data.

But the shame of the CO_2 hockey stick does not end there. The IPCC selected the indirect, inaccurate, and less reliable ice core proxy measurements and rejected highly accurate (better than 3 percent) direct chemical measurements of CO_2 in the atmosphere. German scientist Ernst-Georg Beck has compiled a list of ninety thousand direct measurements of CO_2 in 175 published papers between 1812 and 1961. They show 440 ppm of atmospheric CO_2 in 1820 and 1940, and 390 ppm in 1855, all long before any significant contribution from the burning of fossil fuels by humans. Dr. Jaworowski states that these measurements were rejected by the IPCC "not because they were wrong...The only reason for rejection was that these measurements did not fit the hypothesis of anthropogenic (man-made) global warming. I regard this as perhaps the greatest scandal of our time."

That describes the hockey stick of atmospheric carbon-dioxide used by the IPCC, Al Gore, and the media to claim that carbon emissions are the greatest threat to the planet.

EIGHT

THE GLOBAL WARMING BANDWAGON

The collapse of a scientific foundation for man-made global warming has meant that an entire arsenal of new tactics must be employed to defeat the skeptics and force the alarmists' mandates on the American people—and the picture is not pretty. The strategy involves suppressing the truth about global warming and instilling fear in the public mind—a strategy that requires the active participation of academia, the media, environmental groups, governments worldwide, the United Nations and even religion. The following illustrates the approach adopted and the contributions to this strategy that have been made by these entities:

ACADEMIA

The prevailing attitude in academia on climate change is revealed by Stanford University's climate alarmist Steven Schneider in 1989: "To capture the public imagination, we have to offer up some scary scenarios...Each of us has to decide the right balance between being effective, and being honest."

In 2001, Petr Chylek, Professor of Physics and Atmospheric Science, Dalhousie University, Halifax, Nova Scotia, comments: "Scientists who want to attract attention to themselves, who want to attract great funding to themselves, have to find a way to scare the public...and this you can achieve only by making things bigger and more dangerous than they really are."

MIT atmospheric science professor Richard Lindzen says:

"Scientists who dissent from the alarmism have seen their funds disappear, their work derided, and themselves labeled as industry stooges."

Dr. William Gray, the nation's foremost hurricane expert, has refuted alarmist claims about the effect of global warming on hurricanes. After being attacked by global warming crusaders and his research funding dried up, he put $100,000 of his own funds into his research.

Dr. Timothy Ball, former climatology professor at University of Winnipeg, has received five death threats since he began questioning man-made global warming.

THE MEDIA

The viewing media have become purveyors of false information and fear. Informing the public has become secondary to scaring the public. A fearmongering finale provides the conclusion to every presentation on climate change. Without exception, every network and cable television channel has unquestioningly climbed aboard the global warming bandwagon, with unchallenged acceptance of every radical claim, including Discovery Channel, History Channel, National Geographic Channel, Weather Channel, "fair and balanced" Fox News Channel and even Science Channel.

Massive promotion of fear by the media is illustrated by just a portion of the History Channel's programming in 2007:

In March, climate change was ranked as the deadliest threat to humanity, worse than being fried by nuclear war, or an asteroid impact, or deadly infectious diseases. In November, a program entitled A Global Warning? states that global warming due to greenhouse gases is "the death sentence for humans and other species." The hysteria-generating program contained at least one false statement for every few minutes of programming. In December, a program describes global warming as the "Countdown to Armageddon."

In December 2007, the Science Channel presented Meltdown: A Global Warming and used the fraudulent "hockey stick" of global temperature over the last one thousand years to promote catastrophic warming by greenhouse gases as the cause of the meltdown. On the Science Channel's Planet Earth series in 2008, the views of a parade of environmentalists led to the recommendation that in order to preserve biodiversity and save the planet's species from extinction caused by global warming, the population of the human species must be reduced by at least half. The methods for eliminating half the human species were not addressed, but others have given it some thought. An environmentalist once explained his opposition to eradicating malaria by lifting the thirty-five-year ban on DDT: "Malaria is as good a way to die as any." Sadly, one finds fearmongering and junk-science, not science, on the Science Channel.

CNN made a determination that there could not possibly be nine errors in Al Gore's movie An Inconvenient Truth. A program entitled The Truth about Global Warming was shown on CNN in October 2007 to refute the nine errors found by a British magistrate in his refusal to approve the showing of the movie in British schools. The title misrepresented the content of the program, and only a belief that the public was gullible would lead CNN to attempt to dismiss the judge's conclusions with diversions, selective observations, and irrelevant facts.

Among the print media, Time and Newsweek have been promoting irrational fear about climate change for decades, and time always proves them wrong. Even National Geographic, in magazine and television, has sacrificed credibility by presenting fiction as fact, as in the September 2004 issue of its magazine. In 2008, National Geographic Channel used the most extreme climate model projection on global warming for the title of a program called Six Degrees and asserts that the burning of fossil fuels are "crimes against the climate."

In all of journalism, fact checking has been abandoned and investigative reporting on climate change is nonexistent. Totally invested in promoting doom-and-gloom scenarios, the media have become mere peddlers of false information on Earth's climate. Americans cannot trust what the media tells them about science. It is not science.

ENVIRONMENTAL GROUPS

Environmental groups are always at the forefront of alarmism, pressuring politicians to legislate mandates to restrict individual behavior, because humans are destroying the environment, they say. Their support for the most left-wing politicians is automatic and reflects their endorsement of socialist schemes of regimentation. They have become anticapitalist political, not environmental, organizations.

Since energy is essential to a successful economy, these groups are opposed to all practical forms of energy—fossil fuels because they emit carbon dioxide and nuclear energy which does not. Opposition to nuclear energy proves that global warming alarmism by these so-called environmental groups is a facade. If they truly believed that atmospheric carbon dioxide was the environmental threat that they claim, their thirty-year opposition to nuclear power, with its proven record of safety, would be reversed.

The great danger at present is that pandering politicians will respond to these groups by enacting economy-crippling legislation to fight the nonexistent problem of global warming. Destroy an economy by starving it of energy.

An examination of the record of these groups, such as protecting the malaria-carrying anopheles mosquito with the ban on DDT, leads to the conclusion that the greatest threat to humanity and the environment is the environmentalists.

The groups promoting man-made global warming include the following: Greenpeace, Sierra Club, World Wildlife Fund, American Association for the Advancement of Science, National Wildlife Federation, National Resources Defense Council, Union of Concerned Scientists, Society of Environmental Journalists, and American Bird Conservancy.

RELIGION

Some alarmists have adopted a religious theme to promote global warming—a matter of faith. Global warming must be accepted according to the Biblical obligation to be good stewards of the planet. Al Gore, the high priest of the Church of Global Warming, declared "climate change" was "the most important moral, ethical, spiritual, and political issue humankind has ever faced." As senator, Barack Obama called climate change the most serious threat facing African-American families, and emission cuts are "a faith issue."

Certain evangelical Christians have formed Evangelical Climate Initiative calling for drastic action to halt CO_2 emissions and global warming. Another group, Evangelical Environmental Network, weighs in with the slogan "What Would Jesus Drive?"

But not all evangelicals are willing to be told what must be accepted as a matter of faith. Another group—researchers, professors, and pastors—has formed Interfaith Stewardship Alliance that recognizes the jury is out on whether mankind has had any effect on climate change.

Not all communities of faith are fooled by the diversion from the science of global warming to an appeal as a matter of religious faith.

POLITICS

—The Real Global Warming Crisis

According to Jacques Chirac, the Kyoto Treaty is "the first component of an authentic global government." In the words of Margaret Wallstrom, the European Union's commissioner for the environment, "This is about creating a level playing field for big businesses throughout the world." Canada's environment minister Christine Stewart comments: "No matter if the science is all phony, there are still collateral environmental benefits" to global warming policies..."Climate change provides the greatest chance to bring about justice and equality in the world."

Even Kyoto's proponents acknowledge that, if fully implemented, the Kyoto Protocol would only reduce global warming by an undetectable 0.07°C by 2050. How much would the U.S. economy have been damaged if the U.S. had signed on to the Kyoto Treaty committing the U.S. to cut emissions to 7 percent below the 1990 level? One measure of the harm to the economy required to achieve the hypothetical 0.07°C reduction is the following: If Congress were to outlaw the use of gasoline for all uses, the U.S. would just barely meet the Kyoto target.

A cap-and-trade system is being promoted in Congress in which industries are issued ration coupons called "credits" for the quotas of CO_2 they are permitted to emit. If a company needed more credits, they could be purchased through a so-called market of unused credits. A cap-and-trade program is merely a ruse to raise government revenue from homeowners and other consumers by increasing costs to energy producers. The increased cost imposed on energy suppliers in the purchase of artificial carbon dioxide emission allowances from government is passed along to consumers. Emission limits are progressively reduced in future years with additional energy costs to consumers. Cap-and-trade constitutes a hidden tax on consumers, rationing of energy, another subsidy for renewable energy sources that can't make it on their own, a wealth redistribution beloved by Socialists, and an enrichment scheme for brokers in the artificial market for trading "pollution" credits—like Al Gore. Gore claims his purchase of carbon credits offsets his huge "carbon footprint," but the money passes from one pocket to another through his company Generation Investment Management.

The effect of cap-and-trade on CO_2 in the atmosphere? Not measurable. The reduction in global warming? Zero. The impact on the economy? Depression. How do we know this? Because we've been through it before. Dr. Martin Hertzberg has documented the consequences of a 30 percent worldwide reduction is fossil fuel emissions in the 1930s. Despite this substantial reduction in human emissions, global temperature and atmospheric carbon dioxide continued to increase. Why? Because global temperature is not determined by human activity, and the increase in atmospheric carbon dioxide is from the oceans.

The 30 percent reduction of emissions in the 1930s was associated with the Great Depression. What will we call the economic catastrophe resulting from an 80 percent reduction in the use of fossil fuels by 2050, as proposed by president-elect Obama?

Since the consequences of Kyoto reductions are known to be insignificant, what is really driving the global warming agenda? It is not the environment. It is money. Money for government through cap-and-trade, and money for the global warming industry through government funding. Funding goes to those who claim that global warming is a serious problem that warrants a massive commitment of taxpayer dollars. According to the National Oceanic and Atmospheric Administration's James Maloney in 2004 $20 billion had already been disbursed to the scientific community since 1990. Presently, $5 billion is spent every year on climate research. But global warming researchers are funded by 13 different federal agencies, not just NOAA. After twenty years of research to find evidence supporting the theory of man-made global warming, not against it, and the expenditure of more than 50 billion dollars, not even a fingerprint of a human contribution to global warming has been found.

Many scientists have sold their credibility for a government grant, since research money goes to those promoting climate alarmism. For a researcher to discover that the threat of global warming is exaggerated, funding would be terminated, tenure would be withheld, promotion would be denied, and he would be declared an outcast. It is not funding by oil companies that has corrupted the science of climate change; it is funding by government.

The rhetoric of Jacques Chirac, Margaret Wallstrom, Christine Stewart, United Nations and European bureaucrats and pandering U.S. politicians demonstrates that the ultimate goal of Kyoto advocates is control of all carbon emissions. Control of carbon emissions means control of all life on planet earth—fulfilling a bureaucrat's dream.

The greatest threat to planet Earth is the global warming political agenda, not climate change.

NINE

THE GLOBAL WARMING DEBATE

"The science is settled." "The debate is over." So declare nonscientists Al Gore, Gov. Arnold Schwarzenegger, and former EPA administrator Christine Todd Whitman.

"There is a consensus on climate change," a reference to the reports by some two thousand politically appointed members of the United Nations IPCC. If consensus is important, there is the Oregon petition signed by thirty-two thousand scientists and engineers in opposition to the Kyoto global warming agreement, stating that "limits on greenhouse gases would harm the environment" and that "there is no convincing scientific evidence that human release of greenhouse gases will cause catastrophic heating of the Earth."

In December 2007 and December 2008, reports were submitted to the U.S. Senate containing the comments of more than 650 prominent scientists from more than two dozen countries detailing the reasons they have become skeptics of man-made global warming and voicing objections to the so-called "consensus" of the U.N.'s IPCC. The 2007 Summary for Policymakers was written by fifty-two "political" scientists selected by the IPCC.

"Consensus" on any scientific issue such as global warming is a fictional and nonsensical term—an oxymoron. Scientific truths are determined by scientific evidence, tested and confirmed by other scientists. There is no scientific evidence to support the theory of man-made global warming; there are only computer models that fail to agree with observations in the real world. The science is not settled.

The debate is over? Where was it held, and when? Who participated? The most stunning and disturbing fact about the "debate" over global warming is that there has been no debate. For more than fifteen years, there has been suppression of scientific evidence and debate on global warming. Television viewers have never seen an honest discussion on global warming. They hear about melting polar ice caps, but the fact that ice thickness has been increasing for thirty years over most of Antarctica is a well-kept secret.

Recently, Al Gore refused to appear with scientist Bjorn Lomborg to discuss the claims in his film, An Inconvenient Truth. The History Channel withheld the climatological history of planet Earth that refutes unscientific speculation on climate change and declared without debate that global warming is the deadliest threat to civilization.

The attacks on global warming dissent have taken an ominous tone. Al Gore declares that those who do not accept the theory that humans are to blame for global warming belong to the Flat Earth Society and the media should refuse to interview these global warming deniers. The Weather Channel's Heidi Cullen recommends decertifying climatologists who dissent on global warming. Britain's science advisor Sir David King declares global warming is "the greatest threat facing mankind, worse than terrorism."

Three suppressors of dissent occupy seats in the U.S. Senate. Senators Olympia Snowe of Maine and John D. Rockefeller IV of West Virginia sent an intimidating letter to the chairman of Exxon Mobil criticizing the company for funding "climate change denial" groups. During hearings on the McCain-Lieberman Kyoto-like global warming legislation, Senator John McCain refused to permit testimony from scientists at the George C. Marshall Institute, denigrating the scientists by saying General Marshall would turn over in his grave if he knew what was being done in his name. Three senators use the power of their office to exert Stalinist-like suppression of dissent.

Some of the onslaught on dissent knows no bounds and has become vicious. Yvo de Boer, the United Nations top climate official, says failure to recognize and act on global warming is "nothing less than criminally irresponsible." Greenpeace says global warming skeptics are "climate criminals." Robert Kennedy Jr. rants that skeptics are "traitors." The Boston Globe's Ellen Goodman writes: "global warming deniers are on a par with Holocaust deniers." Grist magazine calls for "Nuremberg-style war crimes trials."

Rajendra Pachauri, chairman of the United Nations IPCC, had this to say about Bjorn Lomborg, author of the The Skeptical Environmentalist, in 2004: "What is the difference between Lomborg's view of humanity and Hitler's?" In 2001, biologist E. O. Wilson described "contrarians like Lomborg" as "parasites."

James Hansen, Al Gore's climate advisor who first demonized greenhouse gases before Congress in 1988, again appeared before Congress twenty years later in June 2008 and called for the trial of oil company executives for "high crimes against humanity and nature" for "actively spreading doubt about global warming." In the twenty-year interval between his appearances, satellite readings show that the Earth had cooled by 0.5°F. With a track record of failure in climate prophecy, James Hansen initiates the Hansen Inquisition against global warming dissent.

Recently it has been learned that Hansen, who is in charge of NASA's temperature data, has tampered with the temperature record by adjusting temperature prior to 1970 downward and the temperatures of recent years upward, to create the impression that the planet is getting still warmer. The doctoring of the data for 2008 included the elimination of readings from most of Canada, Greenland, and Antarctica. Reliable temperature data from the UK's Hadley Center, the University of Alabama at Huntsville, and from two satellite-based systems exposed Hansen's deceit. The same tactic was used by the IPCC with weather stations in cold regions in order to claim the 1990s was the hottest decade on record. Now we know why NASA's global surface temperature record is no longer trusted. There is the urban heat island effect, the extraneous factors that influence weather station readings, the closing of weather stations in cold regions, and the data goes through the hands of James Hansen.

But manipulation of scientific evidence and prosecution of global warming dissent is only the beginning for Mr. Hansen. In 2008, Hansen testified on behalf of three Greenpeace vandals who caused $60,000 worth of damage to a coal-fired power plant. A UK jury accepted the defendants' "lawful excuse" argument that they caused the minimum damage necessary to prevent "imminent peril" to the planet from global warming. Two weeks after the acquittal, Al Gore urged young people in the U.S. to engage in "civil disobedience" to stop the construction of coal-fired plants that do not sequester CO_2 emissions. Sanctioned in the UK and endorsed by Al Gore and James Hansen in the U.S., terrorism is now an approved weapon in their war against global warming.

It is ironic that the accusation of Stalinism that Al Gore levels at his critics in his movie An Inconvenient Truth describes precisely the tactics practiced today by Gore, James Hansen, and their fellow travelers in the alarmist movement.

Global warming has evolved into authoritarianism masquerading as science. Welcome to the global warming wing of environmental fascism.

The science of climate change is not settled. Climate science is an immature science about which little is known. Earth's climate has always changed from natural causes and a human impact has never been detected.

The debate is not over. The debate was never held. Dissent has been suppressed in every debating arena: television and print media, academia, Congress, and the IPCC of the United Nations.

But the skeptics have not been silenced:

Retired Princeton physicist Freeman Dyson has studied climate models and concludes: "They do a very poor job of describing the clouds, the dust, the chemistry and biology of fields and farms and forests. They do not begin to describe the real world that we live in."

Christopher Horner, author of The Politically Incorrect Guide to Global Warming and Environmentalism has compiled a list of the Top Ten Global Warming Myths.

Dr. David Deming of the University of Oklahoma concludes that "global warming hysteria is based on ignorance fueled by speculation and alarmism."

A documentary has appeared on British television entitled The Great Global Warming Swindle.

Timothy Ball, the first Canadian PhD in climatology, has called global warming "the greatest deception in the history of science."

John Coleman, the meteorologist who founded the Weather Channel, has called global warming "a scam. The greatest scam in history...In time, a decade or two, the outrageous scam will be obvious."

Dr. Kiminori Itoh, a member of the UN's IPCC, states that global warming fears are the "worst scientific scandal in history... When people come to know what the truth is, they will feel deceived by science and scientists."

Senator James Inhofe (R-Oklahoma), the most knowledgeable individual in the United States Senate on the science of global warming, has called global warming "the greatest hoax perpetrated on the American people."

One day in the future it will become known that the global warming scam was based on grossly inadequate and erroneous computer models, junk science, hysteria generated by the echo chamber of network and cable television featuring fearmongering speculation by complicit scientists, censorship by the media, suppression of dissent in academia, intimidation by the powerful in government and fraudulent portrayals of past and present global climate by the IPCC of the United Nations.

In 1633, Galileo was tried for heresy for suggesting that the Earth revolved around the Sun, contradicting the consensus view at the time. Just as the skeptic Galileo was right after all, so too will science and the passing of time prove the global warming skeptics were right after all.

TEN

THE TRUTH

The truth about climate change and global warming evolves from the accumulation and correct interpretation of scientific evidence. The evidence must pass the test of peer review and confirmation by other scientists. Interpretation must permit challenge by contradictory evidence and thorough debate. These essential elements are ignored by the media, politically correct academia, the United States Congress and Supreme Court, the European Union and the United Nations IPCC. But they are not ignored in the real world of science. The science of climate and climate phenomena—climatology—is unlike any other science. The Earth's climate is so complex that it requires the collective knowledge from dozens of scientific disciplines and interaction between them, including climatology, meteorology, geology, biology, chemistry, physics, mathematics, paleoclimatology, atmospheric chemistry and physics, and cosmology. Yes, cosmology! In fact, the study of supernovae and the cosmic rays they produce may provide the key to Earth's past and future climate (see section 12)

Individual scientists know a great deal about one piece of the climate puzzle. But there is no single individual who is an authority on all these disciplines. The objective of the guide is to describe in layman's language the evidence that scientists in these disciplines have contributed to an understanding of Earth's climate and the conclusions that may be drawn.

The evidence reveals that global warming hysteria promoted by the IPCC, Al Gore, complicit scientists, and the media is based on fraudulent hockey sticks of global temperature and atmospheric CO_2, and computer models that use the hockey sticks and fudge factors to project catastrophic global warming. Tim Ball and John Coleman have correctly described global warming as "the greatest deception in the history of science" and "the greatest scam in history."

Where can the truth be found? There are journals that still adhere to scientific standards. Many books have been written by scientists with credentials in the disciplines relevant to climatology and other authors with a scientific background who have spent years studying the subject. An example of the latter is the book *State of Fear* by Michael Crichton, author of the popular *Jurassic Park*. These books reference and summarize the scientific literature related to Earth's climate and the books most valuable to the layman are listed in the references. Only an informed public can prevent "The Great Global Warming Swindle" from being pulled off.

ELEVEN

DEFEATING CENSORSHIP

If the most knowledgeable and competent scientists had not had the courage to risk their livelihoods by writing about and discussing the scientific evidence on Earth's climate, and if a few book publishers had failed to risk condemnation in the publishing industry, there would be a complete blackout of truthful information available to the public on global warming.

These scientists have shown that higher levels of carbon dioxide in the atmosphere follow warming of the Earth from natural causes, not the other way around; that the United Nations IPCC has used failed computer models and fraudulent and erroneous data to promote its global warming agenda; that there is no scientific basis for the claim of catastrophic consequences from human greenhouse gas emissions and, therefore, global warming is a hoax. The scientists who have refused to be silenced or censored are identified in the volumes of the reference list.

Censorship of global warming dissent even extends down to the level of newspaper letters to the editor. The appendix of the first edition of this book consists of forty-six letters on global warming, each submitted to eight newspapers over a seven-year period, 2001-2008. The letters were based primarily on the scientific evidence contained in the publications listed in the references. The rejection ratio was over 80 percent. Nine of the letters were rejected by all eight newspapers. This guide to global warming represents one layman's response to suppression of dissent and censorship.

TWELVE

CLOUDS AND COSMIC RAYS

The object that creates Earth's climate—the Sun—is dismissed by the IPCC with the naive statement that variations in solar irradiance of the Earth are too small to account for the changes in Earth's climate. But the Sun does more than bathe the Earth in sunshine. There are eleven-year cycles of solar activity revealed by sunspots. Sunspots are regions of intense magnetic activity on the solar surface. The more sunspots, the greater the solar activity.

Associated with solar activity is the solar wind—a continuous ejection of charged particles from the Sun's surface that travel throughout interplanetary space—and a solar magnetic field that is carried by these charged particles. The solar magnetic field deflects some of the cosmic rays coming from outer space, preventing them from striking Earth's atmosphere. The stronger the magnetic field, the greater the diversion of cosmic rays from our atmosphere.

A Danish scientist, Henrik Svensmark, has found that cosmic rays are directly involved in the formation of clouds, and he has demonstrated the physical mechanism by which cosmic rays ionize air molecules and create condensation nucleii for water vapor and the formation of clouds. When fewer cosmic rays hit the atmosphere (high solar activity), fewer clouds are formed, more of the Sun's radiation strikes Earth's surface, and Earth's climate warms. With more cosmic rays (low solar activity), more clouds are formed and the Earth cools.

In addition to providing the seeds for the creation of water droplets and the formation of clouds, cosmic rays produce radioactive carbon-14 and beryllium-10 in the atmosphere. Precipitation of these elements, combined with their known periods of decay into nonradioactive products, allows their concentration in the atmosphere to be determined in ice cores and geologic core samples. These provide an historical record of variations in the solar magnetic field, cosmic ray intensity and, most importantly, Earth's climate extending hundreds of millions of years into the past.

How significant is the influence of the solar cycle on cloud cover compared to its effect on direct solar illumination? Solar illumination of the Earth averages 342 watts per square meter and varies by only about 0.001 watt per square meter with each cycle of solar activity. From data of Canadian scientist Jan Veizer, each cycle of solar activity results in a variation of cosmic ray flux striking Earth's atmosphere of about 10 percent and a variation in cloud cover of about 3 percent. The change in cloud cover translates into a change in solar illumination of the Earth by about 10 watts per square meter, which represents an amplification of the change in solar illumination of Earth's surface with each solar cycle by a factor of ten thousand. The change due to cloud cover of 10 watts per square meter with each solar cycle of eleven years is four times greater than the 2.4 watts per square meter that the IPCC attributes to man-made global warming for the entire period since the beginning of the industrial age in 1850.

If the effect of solar activity on cloud cover and, therefore, on Earth's climate is so large, shouldn't it be apparent in Earth's climate history? The evidence is substantial and, in comparison to the greenhouse gas hypothesis, overwhelming. Consider the following evidence starting from the earliest times and moving toward the present.

Jan Veizer has extended Earth's climate record to more than 500 million years in the past by examining calcite shells buried in seabed sediments. They show a correlation of Earth's temperature with the flux of cosmic rays but no correlation with atmospheric CO_2, with "icehouse" episodes occurring even when the concentration of CO_2 was 6000 ppm—more than fifteen times higher than today.

Numerous studies by German and Finnish scientists have

demonstrated a strong correlation between variations in global temperature and both sunspot counts and cosmic ray flux, extending over the last eleven thousand years. No correlation exists with atmospheric CO_2. The influence of solar activity on cosmic rays is identified with nine warming-cooling cycles roughly fifteen hundred years long since the end of the last ice age. The most recent cycle consists of the four-hundred-year-long Medieval Warm Period with temperature up to 2°C (4°F) warmer than today, and the five-hundred-year-long Little Ice Age with temperatures 2°C cooler than today. During the 20th century, Earth has been in the warming phase of the next cycle, but the cycle has peaked and begun to decline.

Several studies have compared global temperature with solar cycle amplitude, cycle length, and the envelope of cycle amplitudes, demonstrating a correlation with temperature extending eighteen hundred years in the past. Jan Veizer has found a remarkable correlation between the cycles of solar activity and global temperature throughout the last millennium, including both the Medieval Warm Period and the Little Ice Age. Particularly striking is the clear correspondence between low solar activity and the four cold periods of the Little Ice Age (the Wolf minimum, 1300–1360; the Sporer Minimum, 1450-1540; the Maunder Minimum, 1645-1715; the Dalton Minimum, 1790-1820), as well as reduced solar activity during the cool period of the 20th century (1960s-1970s).

The global warming of the 20th century coincided with the highest level of solar activity over the last eight thousand years, rising by a factor of 2.3 since 1901. Solar activity began to decline in 2000, sunspots are disappearing, and a steep decline is expected for at least the next two eleven-year cycles. The decline means increased cloud cover and an extensive period of global cooling in the years ahead. Satellites reveal that cloud cover is increasing and no global warming, even a slight cooling, has been observed since 2000, despite increased CO_2 in the atmosphere. A decline of 0.75°C (1.35°F) over eighteen months in 2007-8 wipes out the entire increase over the last century. If the next two cycles are as weak as anticipated from the climate record, it is estimated that the world can look forward to a cooling by 1.5°C (2.7°F) in the decades ahead.

There is even more reason to expect that global cooling is on the horizon, not global warming. Russia's foremost authority on solar activity and its effect on climate, Dr. Habibullo Abdussamatov, observes that in addition to the eleven-year cycle of solar activity, there is a longer two-hundred-year envelope of solar cycle amplitudes that will extend the decline of solar activity over several of the upcoming eleven-year cycles. He anticipates a cooling reminiscent of the Little Ice Age that will last a century. His prediction is supported by the historical record of the cycles of solar activity.

Conclusion: Earth's climate responds to solar activity—warming when it is high, cooling when it is low. The most remarkable finding in recent climate research is the discovery by Henrik Svensmark of the link between solar activity, cosmic rays, and cloud cover in Earth's lower atmosphere. Svensmark calculates that a change in cloud cover of only a few percent would change global temperature by about 1°C. The total increase in global temperature over the last century of 0.6°C (1°F) can be accounted for by a few percent decrease in cloud cover. Fewer clouds, not more CO_2, account for the global warming of the last century.

It is astounding that the cooling effect of clouds is not recognized in the computer models of the IPCC (it is one of the unknowns in the black box of ignorance). Every human being on Earth has experienced an immediate and dramatic cooling when the Sun disappears behind a cloud. Ignoring the variation in cloud cover that occurs with each solar cycle is one of the fatal flaws of climate models. Cooling by clouds, like truthful data on CO_2 in the atmosphere, does not fit the "preconceived idea of manmade global warming."

If the IPCC were truly interested in a scientific explanation of climate change, it would abandon the dead-end of man-made global warming and examine how Earth's climate is governed by the Sun and cosmic rays, and water. All of the greenhouse gas contributors blamed for climate change—carbon dioxide generated by humans, methane generated by bovine flatulence, etc.—amount to nothing more than, in the blunt layman's language of retired navy meteorologist Dr. Martin Hertzberg in Nation Magazine of 14 May 2007, "a few farts in a hurricane." Dr. Hertzberg has placed man-made global warming and global climate change in proper perspective.

Thirteen

The True Causes of Climate Change

Since CO_2 in the atmosphere does not govern Earth's climate (see Myth #28), what does? Although climate science is in its infancy, much is known nevertheless. It is becoming vital for regular Americans to learn the essentials of Earth's climate, not only to protest the draconian measures about to be mandated by government, but also for the day when a child comes home from school brainwashed by a required viewing of Al Gore's fantasy film in science class.

The truth about Earth's climate has become an essential aspect of a child's education. Because the media and public schools are a font of misinformation, this will only be provided by informed parents. The parents will have to demonstrate that they know more about climate change than today's science teachers. It can be done. Here is how to do it:

(1) Point out that a British judge found more than nine false or unproven claims in Al Gore's movie and refused to allow its viewing in British schools unless alternate views were presented.

(2) Identify the false claims in Gore's movie (Myths #4, 5, 10, 11, 12, 16, 18, 25, and 26). For emphasis, stress that the British judge did not address all of the lies in Gore's movie.

(3) Provide the scientific reasons that atmospheric CO_2 cannot be responsible for climate change or cause catastrophic global warming (myth #28).

(4) Identify the real causes of climate change: The natural phenomena that govern Earth's climate. The following is a list of those phenomena, the magnitude and direction of the change in climate (warming or cooling), and the duration of the change:

(a) The dominant factor in Earth's climate for the past 2 million years has been the occurrence of an ice age every one hundred thousand years. Each ice age consists of a glacial period lasting eighty-five to ninety thousand years, with a drastic reduction in Earth's temperature by 10-12°C (18-22°F), and an interglacial warm period spanning ten to fifteen thousand years. Ice ages are the result of periodic changes in the shape of Earth's orbit and distance from the Sun. The present interglacial warm period has lasted ten thousand years.

(b) It is not just distance from the Sun that controls Earth's climate but the violent activity of the Sun itself. Superimposed on the glacial-interglacial intervals of severe temperature shift are at least three cycles of solar activity that produce more moderate changes in Earth's temperature. Regions of intense magnetic activity on the surface of the Sun are revealed by an eleven-year cycle of sunspots. The strength and duration of each sunspot cycle is reflected in a change in global temperature by typically 0.5°C (1°F). A two-hundred-year cycle provides an envelope of modulation on the series of eleven-year sunspot cycles. The entire 20th century was in the warming phase of this cycle. The cooling phase lies just ahead. A further modulation in a roughly fifteen-hundred-year cycle is reflected most recently in the

Medieval Warm Period followed by the Little Ice Age. The coldest period of the Little Ice Age was about 2°C (4°F) colder than today for about seventy years.

The physical mechanism by which solar activity warms or cools the Earth through its influence on cosmic rays and cloud formation is described in section 12. A variation in cloud cover of only a few percent is sufficient to change Earth's average temperature by 1°C (2°F), which is more than the change observed in the last century.

(c) Solar flares are another form of solar eruption. These energetic bursts send charged particles that create auroras at the poles and disturb radio signals on Earth. Solar flares increased the Sun's ultraviolet radiation on Earth by at least 16 percent in the last century. The magnitude of this change means that short-term climatic effects of solar flares can no longer be ignored.

(d) The reduction in solar illumination by the volcanic eruptions of El Chichon in 1983 and Mt. Pinatubo in 1991 produced cooling by 0.6°C (1°F) for about two years.

(e) The El Nino warming of ocean surface waters in the Pacific raises temperature in the lower atmosphere by about 0.6°C (1°F) for about two years. El Ninos occur every four to seven years. There have been six El Nino warnings since 1980. The IPCC's report in 2007 attributes the warming to greenhouse gas emissions.

(f) Other phenomena that influence climate over vast regions include the flow of cold air masses from the polar regions and the circulation of ocean currents. Some phenomena have earned recognition with the names North Atlantic Oscillation, North Pacific Oscillation, Arctic Oscillation, and Pacific Decadal Oscillation. A particularly unusual change in climate occurred in 1976-77 when the Great Pacific Climate Shift resulted in an abrupt warming of the entire Pacific region by about 0.5°C (1°F). The cause is unknown, but the eruption of an undersea volcano has been suggested. The single jump in temperature in one year explains the entire warming trend over the last half of the 20th century. This temperature burp is part of the warming that the IPCC attributes to humans, even though there is no burp in the IPCC's record of atmospheric CO_2.

For the UN's IPCC and its climate models, a minor constituent in the atmosphere is more powerful than the known major influences on Earth's climate and the modelers are committed to the preconceived notion that humans are the cause of global warming. But the climate record and the laws of physics prove that CO2 in the atmosphere does not cause global warming, even when the puny contribution from humans is added. CO2 in the atmosphere is the result of global warming—a result of global warming produced by natural causes.

The IPCC's computer models predicting catastrophic man-made global warming constitute a virtual world of "what if" computer games played with a CO2 cursor. Alarmist prophecies refuted by science describes the global warming hoax. In the words of author Vladimir Nabokov: "Prophecy is the wit of a fool."

Fourteen

Halting Climate Change

With the collapse of scientific evidence to support the theory of man-made global warming, hysteria and fear have become the driving forces behind the theory. The state of fear created by activists and the media has convinced politicians that legislation to "halt climate change" is a vote-getter.

What laws are legislators going to enact to prevent the climate from changing for the first time in the 4.5-billion-year history of planet Earth? They have already begun.

In December 2007, Congress passed and President Bush signed an energy bill that includes the following:

(1) A ban on one of the most important inventions of the Industrial Age—Thomas Edison's incandescent lightbulb. The ban begins with the 100-watt bulb in 2012 and ends with the 40-watt in 2014. The safe, reliable, inexpensive incandescent lightbulb is to be replaced by costly compact fluorescent bulbs containing the environmental toxin mercury. The mandate means that compact fluorescent bulbs will become a more significant source of environmental mercury than coal-fired power plants. Lawmakers have declared that mercury in the environment is less harmful than nonpolluting carbon dioxide in the atmosphere. True environmentalists know better and will start stocking up on environmentally friendly Edison lightbulbs.

(2) A mandate for a five-fold increase in ethanol from gasoline, diverting farmland from food production to fuel production. A gallon of fossil fuel plus seventeen hundred gallons of water is required in corn production to produce a gallon of ethanol. Only Congress could create legislation to reduce carbon emissions that fails to reduce carbon emissions.

(3) A 40 percent increase in vehicle mileage standards (CAFE) to 35 miles per gallon by the year 2020. In 2001, the National Academy of Sciences found that the present mileage standard contributed to between thirteen hundred and twenty-six hundred traffic deaths every year, by forcing the production of smaller and lighter cars. For Congress public safety is secondary to the demands of global warming activists.

The response of Congress to global warming hysteria is an energy bill that provides no new energy; restricts vehicle choice; mandates and subsidizes costly, unreliable, and inefficient alternative fuels; and imposes other restrictions on American consumers. Nevertheless, California, twelve northeastern states, several cities, and environmental groups have filed suit against the federal government for not imposing emissions restrictions on the American people fast enough. Anticipating a bonanza, law firms are gearing up for the global warming litigation that will follow tobacco and asbestos as the next pot of gold for lawyers.

There's more to come. Next will be some version of the McCain-Lieberman federal legislation mandating Kyoto-like limits on CO_2 emissions by U.S. industry, including a cap-and-trade system of emission credits known to be a failure in the European Union. Numerous analyses have concluded that this so-called Climate Security Act will cause substantial increases in electricity and fuel bills and the loss of several million jobs, with no measurable impact on the climate. Additional burdens may be imposed beginning with a 50-cent-per-gallon tax on gasoline.

But global warming extremists are never satisfied. Al Gore advises Congress to adopt his ten-point plan of a freeze on carbon emissions, a carbon polluter tax, market controls, and regulations representing a massive expansion of government control over the economy. He continues to endorse the Kyoto Protocol which could reduce U.S. gross domestic product by 100 to 400 billion dollars a year, according to the U.S. Energy Information Administration.

During the 2008 primary election, Senators Barack Obama and Hillary Clinton announced plans for limiting carbon emissions even more restrictive and costly than Al Gore's but just as ineffective. As president-elect, Barack Obama promises to "bankrupt" the companies that build coal-fired power plants with greenhouse gas fees. Coal-fired power plants produce 50 percent of the nation's electricity. He wants a cap-and-trade program on fossil fuels to slash carbon dioxide "impurities" by 80 percent by 2050. Laws restricting carbon emissions will cripple the nation's economy and impose a lower standard of living on Americans, but they will not halt climate change. What will be said about a nation that destroyed its economy fighting the phantom of global warming? In his inaugural address, President Obama promised to "roll back the specter of a warming planet." Al Gore's con game will now be orchestrated from the White House.

There's more. The U.S. Environmental Protection Agency has proposed a tax on farm animals as a way to regulate greenhouse gas emissions under the Clean Air Act: $175 per dairy cow, $87.50 a head for beef cattle, and $20 per hog. When flatulence from cows warrants a tax to save the planet from global warming, can a tax on human flatulence be far behind? Furthermore, humans exhale air containing about 50,000 ppm of CO_2. What will be the carbon tax on breathing? There are no limits to the idiocy of government bureaucrats in dealing with a nonexistent threat.

The alarmists fear that the public is beginning to recognize that "global warming pollution" is a myth, so they are pressing for immediate federal action on climate change, mandating, at a minimum, an 80 percent reduction in greenhouse gas emissions by 2050 and a cap-and-trade scam for raising federal revenue. But economy-crippling legislation when the economy is in crisis is an obstacle. They argue that "you can't have a strong economy without a healthy environment." But a look at the economies of the world and their environments reveals the opposite: you don't have a healthy environment without a strong economy.

There is another obstacle—cold weather. The public doesn't buy the alarmists' false claim that global warming causes global cooling. With frigid temperatures and record snowfalls on the first day of winter in 2008, the public has more trustworthy evidence of Earth's climate than college professors with government grants or science teachers who use an Al Gore movie as their climate Bible. To paraphrase Abraham Lincoln, you can fool all of the people some of the time—but not all of the time. It remains to be seen whether the next administration will learn the wisdom of Lincoln.

As politicians proceed to save the planet with costly, misguided global warming legislation, they should be asked one question: "Identify one piece of scientific evidence that proves that humans are the cause of global warming." There is none. All of the evidence proves the contrary. The legislation is a sham. Government mandates will be based on the mythology, not science, of global warming.

It is understandable if most Americans looked at these actions of legislators as laughable. But this is not about halting the phantom threat of man-made global warming. It is about using the fear of global warming to limit individual freedom and control individual behavior. "It's not about saving the planet," writes Paul Driessen. "Saving the planet" is the smokescreen for acquiring the power to control and limit the use of energy. It's about humans being deprived of liberty, property, and life itself.

On February 15 2008, the mayor of the city victimized by terrorists on 9/11, Michael Bloomberg, declared that global warming was a greater threat than both terrorism and the proliferation of nuclear weapons. It is one thing for the History Channel to entertain viewers by ranking climate change as a greater threat than nuclear war, an asteroid impact, or a supervolcanic eruption. It is quite another for those exercising the powers of government to fabricate false fear in the minds of the governed. Freedoms are the target, and when the powerful exploit a climate of fear to address a nonexistent problem, freedoms disappear. If the government can deny its people the freedom to purchase the safe, reliable incandescent lightbulb, with the absurd assertion that it contributes to global warming, what further restrictions will be imposed by government?

Consider proposals being advocated elsewhere. In Britain, the Optimum Population Trust calls on Britons to voluntarily reduce the number of children they have. In the Medical Journal of Australia, professor Barry Walters wants a carbon tax of $5000 on each newborn child and an annual carbon tax of $800 per child to offset the carbon emissions generated over each child's lifetime. Female activists in Britain boast of having abortions and being sterilized to save the planet. Professor David Benetar of the University of Cape Town argues "it would be better if humanity became extinct." For some, the solution to man-made global warming is the elimination of man.

If omnipotent lawyers and scientifically challenged legislators believe they can "halt climate change" with legislation, they must first eliminate the causes of climate change in the past. Here is what must be done: ban the eruption of volcanoes, prohibit asteroids from entering Earth's atmosphere, and eliminate the eleven-year cycle of solar activity. Preventing the next ice age will require legislation altering the Earth's orientation and orbit about the Sun. But to prove the allegation that humans are causing climate change, they must turn off the Sun and measure how much the emissions from humans, hogs, and cows are warming the planet.

Any other legislated measure will constitute an assault on the liberty and economic well-being of the American people and a disruptive exercise in futility. When the science of global warming and climate change can no longer be ignored, suppressed, or censored, the promoters of the man-made global warming hoax will no longer be able to impose an authoritarian agenda through fear and hysteria.

Students of history will see parallels with the past. Listen to the rhetoric of alarmists in government. "Saving the planet from climate change" and "fighting the war against global warming" are "too important for democracy." Al Gore's "climate crisis" is "resolvable only through totalitarian means" and "an ecodictatorship is needed."

Numerous researchers have noted the striking similarity between the Green Party and Fascist ideologies in Germany, as well as the Stalinist-like enforcement of the socialist ideology beloved by global warming alarmists. UN officials and Al Gore's science advisor have opened the door to consideration of gulags for skeptics.

The guide concludes by asking a very important question: Will the IPCC, Al Gore, James Hansen, the media, and the rest of the global warming industry succeed in squelching scientific evidence and suppressing, even criminalizing, dissent? It would be a stunning and truly man-made catastrophe if the hoax of man-made global warming provided the foundation for the triumph of tyranny over liberty.

REFERENCES

1. Patrick J. Michaels, *Sound and Fury: The Science and Politics of Global Warming*. Washington, D.C.: Cato Institute 1993.

2. Ronald Bailey, *Eco-Scam: The False Prophets of Ecological Apocalypse*. New York: St. Martin's Press, 1993

3. Wilfred Beckerman, *Through Green-Colored Glasses: Environmentalism Reconsidered*. Washington, D.C.: Cato Institute 1996.

4. Ron Arnold, *Ecology Wars: Environmentalism As If People Mattered*. Bellevue, Washington: Free Enterprise Press, 1993.

5. Thomas Gale Moore, *Climate-of Fear: Why We Shouldn't Worry about Global Warming*, Washington, D.C.: Cato Institute, 1998.

6. Steven Milloy and Michael Gough, *Silencing Science*. Washington, D.C.: Cato Institute, 1998.

7. Peter Huber, *Hard Green: Saving the Environment from the Environmentalists*. New York: Basic Books, 1999.

8. S. Fred Singer, *Hot Talk, Cold Science: Global Warming's Unfinished Debate*. Oakland, California: The Independent Institute, 1999.

9. Bjorn Lomborg, *The Skeptical Environmentalist: Measuring the Real State of the World*. Cambridge: Cambridge University Press, 2001.

10. Patrick J. Michaels and Robert C. Balling, Jr., *The Satanic* Gases: Clearing the Air about Global Warming Washington, D.C.: Cato Institute, 2000.

11. Ronald Bailey, Editor, *Global Warming and other Eco-Myths: How the Environmental Movement Uses False Science to Scare Us to Death*. Roseville, California: Prima Publishing, 2002.

12. Kendra Okonski, Editor, *Adapt or Die: The Science, Politics and Economics of Climate Change.* London: Profile Books Ltd., 2003.

13. Michael Gough, Editor, *Politicizing Science, the Alchemy of Policymaking.* George C. Marshall Institute: Hoover Institution Press, 2003.

14. Jack W. Dini, *Challenging Environmental Mythology: Wrestling Zeus.* Raleigh, NC: Sci Tech Publishing, 2003.

15. Michael Crichton, *State of Fear.* New York: Harper Collins Publishers, 2004.

16. Howard C. Hayden, *The Solar Fraud: Why Solar Energy Won't Run The World.* Pueblo, CO: Vales Lake Publishing, 2004.

17. Patrick J. Michaels, *Meltdown: The Predictable Distortion of Global Warming by Scientists, Politicians, and the Media.* Washington, D.C.: Cato Institute, 2004.

18. National Geographic Magazine, *Global Warming: Bulletins from a Warmer World.* National Geographic Society, September 2004.

19. Patrick J. Michaels, Editor, *Shattered Consensus: The True State of Global Warming.* Lanham, Maryland: Rowman and Littlefield Publishers, 2005.

20. Marcel Leroux, *Global Warming - Myth or Reality: The Erring Ways of Climatology.* Chichester, UK: Praxis Publishing Ltd., 2005.

21. S. Fred Singer and Dennis T. Avery, *Unstoppable Global Warming: Every 1,500 Years.* Lanham, Maryland: Rowman and Littlefield Publishers 2007.

22. Time, *Global Warming: The Causes, The Perils, The Solutions, The Actons: What You Can Do.* New York: Time Books, 2007.

23. Christopher C. Horner, *The Politically Incorrect Guide-to Global*

Warming and Environmentalism. Washington, D.C.: Regnery Publishing, 2007.

24. Ernst-Georg Beck, *180 Years of Atmospheric CO_2 Gas Analysis by Chemical Methods.* Energy and Environment, Vol. 18, No.2, 2007.

25. Ross R. McKitrick and Patrick J. Michaels, Journal of Geophysical Research 112, December 2007.

26. N.D.Marsh and H. Svensmark, Physical Review Letters, Volume 85, 5004-5007, 2000.

27. Jan Veizer, Geoscience Canada, Volume 32, 13-28, March 2005.

28. Environment and Climate News. Chicago, IL: The Heartland Institute.

29. Arthur B. Robinson, Noah E. Robinson, and Willie Soon, Environmental Effects of Increased Atmospheric Carbon Dioxide. Journal of American Physicians and Surgeons, Volume 12, 79-90, 2007.

30. Howard C. Hayden, *A Primer on CO 2 and Climate (Second Edition).* Pueblo West, CO: Vales Lake Publishing, 2008.

31. Lawrence Solomon, The Deniers. Richard Vigilante Books, 2008.

32. Roy W. Spencer, *Climate Confusion.* New York: Encounter Books, 2008.

33. Steve Milloy, The Real "Inconvenient Truth," at http://www.junkscience.com/Greenhouse/

34. Christopher Monckton, Climate chaos? Don't believe it. United Kingdom, Sunday Telegraph, 5 November 2006.

35. Henrik Svensmark and Nigel Calder, The *Chilling Stars.* Cambridge, UK: Icon Books Ltd, 2008.

36. Christopher Essex and Ross McKitrick, *Taken by Storm*. Toronto, Canada: Key Porter Books, 2007.

37. R. M. Carter, The Myth of Dangerous Human-Caused Climate Change. The AusIMM New Leaders' Conference, Brisbane, QLD, 2-3 May 2007.

38. Zbigniew Jaworowski, CO_2. The greatest scientific scandal of our time, Executive Intelligence Review 34(11): 38-53 (2007).

39. Christopher C. Horner, *Red Hot Lies*. Washington, D.C.: Regnery Publishing, 2008.

About the Author

This Guide was not prepared by a meteorologist with experience in making 5-day weather forecasts, nor a climatologist concerned with longer range predictions of regional weather patterns. It was not written by a politician looking for consensus to reach a compromise on a scientific issue. It was prepared by a retired physicist who adheres to the scientific method to reach conclusions about a scientific problem. Global warming due to greenhouse gases and the broader subject of climate change are scientific issues.

Twenty eight years of research experience in laser physics and materials science at Bell Laboratories instilled a desire to understand the scientific basis for the predictions in the 1990s of climate catastrophe by the year 2100.

Both graduate school research in infrared physics at Syracuse University and professional work on infrared lasers provided the background needed to appreciate global warming resulting from the absorption and emission of infrared radiation by greenhouse gases in the atmosphere.

More than ten years later, the greenhouse effect remains an interesting phenomenon in infrared physics. But scientific evidence and analysis by the most competent scientists reveals that global warming by greenhouse gases in the atmosphere will not result in catastrophic warming of planet Earth, and that global warming being caused by carbon dioxide in the atmosphere is a scientific hoax.

CPSIA information can be obtained at www.ICGtesting.com
Printed in the USA
LVOW12s2139030914

402274LV00001B/382/P